THE HORMONE QUEST

●

BOOKS BY *Albert Q. Maisel*

Miracles of Military Medicine
Africa
The Wounded Get Back
They All Chose America
The Hormone Quest

THE
HORMONE
QUEST

•

Albert Q. Maisel

Random House   New York

FOR DUTSA

•

INTRODUCTION

•

Within all our bodies there exists a group of small capsules of tissue, the endocrine glands. The largest, the pancreas, has an average weight of less than three ounces. The smallest, the pineal gland, is barely large enough to cover the period that ends this sentence. Add in all the others— the thyroid, the four parathyroids, the twin adrenals, the pituitary, the thymus, and the paired ovaries of women or testes of men—and the entire battery would tip the scale at between four and seven ounces.

Yet it is these few bundles of very special cells that make us what we are. Throughout our lives they regulate the

activities of all the other cells of our bodies. They control
the processes by which we digest our foods and rebuild
them into blood, bone, muscle, and brain tissue. They
largely determine the length of our bones, the deposition of
fat, and whether we shall be short, stout, tall, thin. They
pace the beating of our hearts and supervise the working
of our livers and kidneys. They time the onset of puberty,
control the menstrual cycles, and govern the many-staged
processes of reproduction, from the first ripening of an egg
cell to the final muscle contractions that propel an infant
toward independent life. They play infinitely varied roles
in determining our mental and emotional development.
And when we are under attack—by bomb or by bacterium
—they mobilize our vital defense mechanisms.

When they function in perfect concert, we are well and
happy. When their delicate balance is upset, we may
suffer from a host of disease processes, from arthritis to
heart attacks, from allergies to ulcers.

They accomplish their myriad activities by generating
fantastically potent chemical compounds called hormones.
Throughout her lifetime, for example, the average woman
produces barely one fifth of an ounce of the female sex
hormones estrogen and progesterone. But the very con-
tinuation of the human race depends upon the exquisite
timing of the release of minuscule amounts of these powerful molecules.

Until barely a hundred years ago the existence of hormones was unknown, and even at the start of this century,
physicians and other scientists had only the most limited
knowledge of the functions of just a few hormones. Yet
even then a few pioneers of endocrine research clearly envisioned the tremendous benefits mankind would gain if
the multiple mysteries enshrouding the endocrine glands

and their hormones could be solved. Thus, Ernest Henry Starling, one of the towering figures of early hormone research, wrote in the *Lancet* in August of 1905: "If control of the different functions of the body be largely determined by the production of definite chemical substances within the body, the discovery of the nature of these substances will enable us to interpose at any desired phase in these functions and so to acquire an absolute control over the workings of the human body. Such a control is the goal of medical science."

By the 1920s and 1930s Starling's successors—a new breed of hormone physiologists and hormone chemists— had learned how to extract a number of the natural hormones from the glands, the bile, and the urine of animals. And a new breed of medical specialists, the endocrinologists, had discovered how to use these extracts to compensate for failure of the human glands to produce their vital hormones with proper timing and in precisely the required quantities. First with thyroid extracts, then with insulin, and gradually with a whole array of extracts, they began saving tens of thousands of lives each year, restoring hundreds of thousands to health and vigor.

During the 1940s and 1950s hormone researchers went much further, synthesizing duplicates of the natural hormones and ingenious modifications of hormone structures even more active than the natural hormones themselves. And pharmaceutical manufacturers learned how to free this young science from its dependence upon limited supplies of hormones extracted from animal tissues; how to make hormones from inexpensive plant materials and even from common chemicals. Compounds that once had cost a king's ransom became available for all who needed them.

More recently, hormone scientists have turned their

synthetic products to a new use in an attempt to help mankind control its runaway fertility. With the development of these birth control compounds, endocrine science has transcended its original role as guardian and restorer of individuals' health. Today it is playing an ever larger role as a major social force, as the agency through which humanity may yet avoid the famines, the plagues, the poverty, and the holocausts of war which seem the inevitable consequences of unlimited human proliferation.

For nearly twenty years it has been my privilege to observe closely and continuously the development of the hormone sciences, from the inside as it were. My first introduction to hormone research came about by sheer chance late in the fall of 1946 when I was commissioned by one of my editors to write a profile of Harvard's great astronomer, Harlow Shapley. But when I arrived at Cambridge, Professor Shapley modestly tried to persuade me that his life and his achievements "really wouldn't make much of a story at all." And when that effort failed, his shyness took another tack. "If you want to do a truly exciting story," he told me, "why don't you write about the Worcester Foundation for Experimental Biology, a unique research institution that is supported, just like a symphony orchestra, by its community."

We compromised then, and I promised to visit the Worcester Foundation *after* I completed his profile. But when I carried out my promise I found myself quickly diverted from an interest in the Foundation's community support to a much deeper interest in the work going on at the infant institution.

I met the co-directors of the Foundation, Drs. Hudson Hoagland and Gregory Pincus, both still in their early forties but with long records of distinguished research achievement at Harvard, at Cambridge University in England, and as Professors of Physiology at Clark University. That morning, in their crowded laboratories in the attic of what was then the Foundation's only building, they began to describe in fascinating detail the studies they had conducted on pilots and test pilots; studies that had revealed the effects of fatigue upon the output of adrenocortical hormones and thus made possible some degree of prediction as to which pilots might best be able to function in moments of stress or crisis.

At lunch they told me how they had discovered that a synthetic steroid, pregnenolone, helped pilots to fly under severe stress with less fatigue than they had previously suffered. And in the afternoon, they took me to the Worcester State Hospital and—together with Drs. Harry Freeman, William Malamud, and the late Roy G. Hoskins—showed me how the same stress-testing techniques they had developed for the Army were being used to compare the reactions to stress of schizophrenics and normal subjects, and were revealing deviations from the normal in the hormone excretion patterns of the mentally ill.

I had come for a one-day visit. But that night I stayed up until 4 A.M. while Pincus and Hoagland explained the implications of their findings. The next morning—my scheduled departure forgotten—I was introduced to Dr. Oscar Hechter who showed me the unique perfusion apparatus he and Dr. Pincus had developed. In this device an adrenal gland removed from an animal was maintained alive and active with pumped blood circulating through it, while it continued to produce adrenal hormones in recoverable quantities.

Later that day I met Dr. Min-Chueh Chang who demonstrated the methods he and Dr. Pincus had developed to stimulate the ovaries of rabbits with hormones so that far more than the normal number of egg cells were released. He showed me the techniques by which they fertilized these ova and transplanted them to the wombs of foster-mother rabbits, where they matured as normal fetuses.

In Dr. Nicholas Werthessen's lab I learned how deviations from the normal had been detected in the hormone-excretion patterns of cancer victims, and how hormones were beginning to be used to arrest the development of certain cancers. And in the cluttered laboratory of the late Dr. Robert P. Jacobsen, I discovered the chemical magic by which synthetic hormones were created and the methods by which their effects were determined through controlled studies on laboratory animals.

My one-day look-see had now stretched to a week-long, intensive course in hormone chemistry and physiology. When I left the Foundation at last, I knew I had found much more than the one good article Dr. Shapley had pointed me toward. I had discovered what science reporters dream about: a vast, growing, and—until then—all too little known field of research that promised to produce immeasureable benefits for the health of mankind.

In the years since that first visit I have returned again and again to the Worcester Foundation. The number of my friends there gradually grew to several dozen, as the Foundation itself earned ever increasing support for its expanding research from its friends and Trustees, from the Navy, the Public Health Service, the American Cancer Society, and from such far-sighted pharmaceutical houses as Ciba, Lilly, Merck Sharp & Dohme, Smith Kline & French, Warner-Lambert and G. D. Searle & Co. And through these Worcester Foundation friends, I met and came to know dozens of others at the cutting edge of hormone research.

In Mexico, Dr. I. V. Sollins revealed to me the manner in which the barbasco plant was uprooted and gathered in the tropical hill forests and shipped to Mexico City to be transformed through intricate chemical processes into the precursor materials of synthetic hormones. At the Université de Montréal, Dr. Hans Selye explained to me his theory of the stress syndrome, a concept which clarified for countless other scientists the complex relationships among the various endocrine glands and the manner in which these normally function to protect us from both mental and physical stress and sometimes fail some of us when stress becomes too intense or too prolonged.

From the gentle and wise Drs. Hannah and Abraham Stone, I learned of all the long struggles they had weathered in the fight to make birth control information available to women, and of their parallel efforts to relieve the infertility of those who desperately wanted children. From the late Dr. Cornelius Rhoads, head of New York's Memorial Hospital, and from Dr. Charles B. Huggins, Professor of Surgery at the University of Chicago, I learned how hormones increasingly were being used in the treatment of cancer.

At the New York Hospital, Dr. John MacLeod introduced me to the extensive studies he and others were conducting on the male role in the physiology of reproduction, and on the relief of hormonal and other causes of infertility in men. At the Rockefeller Foundation, the late Dr. Warren Nelson patiently explained to me the many ways in which researchers the world over were seeking physiological means of birth control.

In the early days of the use of hormones for the relief of rheumatoid arthritis, I "sat in" on Dr. Freddy Homburger's treatment of the French artist Raoul Dufy, and witnessed the almost miraculous remission of his disease, enabling his once crippled hands to lift his brushes and paint again. Later, scores of other outstanding researchers —most notably Drs. John Rock, Celso Ramon Garcia, Abraham White, Robert W. Kistner, Robert B. Greenblatt, Elliot V. Newman, and Abraham E. Rakoff—generously devoted endless hours of their time to my education in the intricacies of hormone therapy.

Drs. Elijah Romonoff, Ralph Dorfman, Erwin Schwenk, Percy Julian, Howard J. Ringold, Sylvia and James Tate, and Ian Bush—all, at one time or another, enlarged my knowledge of the growing achievements of synthetic hormone chemistry.

And in the fine laboratories of G. D. Searle & Co., I have become immeasurably indebted to Drs. Albert L. Raymond, Byron Riegel, I. C. Winter, Victor A. Drill, Frank B. Colton, Kurt Rorig, Francis J. Saunders, William C. Stewart, Robert R. Burtner, E. H. Ensor, Raphael Pappo, G. R. Venning, and Messrs. John G. Searle, Daniel C. Searle, William L. Searle, James W. Irwin, and Franklin P. O'Brien. All of these—and many others—have patiently borne with my questions and freely shared their specialized knowledge.

This volume then is the story of the ever growing role hormones have assumed in the relief of innumerable ailments and in mankind's long struggle to control its fertility. It is also the story of the heroic figures of hormone research, living and dead, whose insight and skill and devotion have brought the hormone sciences to their present advanced state.

But it is an unfinished story. For beyond their already great achievements, the hormone scientists have solidly based dreams of accomplishing far, far more in the not far distant future. They envision the development of hormones —and techniques of using them—to control growth, to prevent or halt cancer and heart diseases, to ward off many of the ravages of age, to save millions from mental illness, and in many other ways to permit man to transcend nature and control his destiny.

Today these goals can be described only under the cautious labels, "hopes" and "dreams." But as I look back upon the hormone researchers' dreams of two decades ago, now transformed into concrete realities, I can see no reason to doubt the realization—within my own lifetime—of almost all of these great goals toward which thousands of scientists and clinicians now are striving.

AUTHOR'S NOTE

One word of caution: Nothing in this book should be construed by any reader as medical advice. Such advice can properly be given only by a competent physician, and even then, only after a thorough study of the individual patient.

CONTENTS

THE HORMONE QUEST

●

1
•

FALSE STARTS AND

WIDE DETOURS

•

It was 1848, the year in which revolutions swept through all the German states. In the university town of Göttingen students and professors debated far into the nights over manifestoes and counter-manifestoes. But one of Göttingen's professors was conspicuous at these meetings only by his absence: Professor Arnold Adolph Berthold was completely preoccupied with a secret project of his own.

Herr Dr. Berthold's secrecy had nothing to do with

political plotting. It stemmed rather from a fear that his colleagues and his students might laugh at his strange experiment; and that, in fact, was why Dr. Berthold did not do this work in his laboratory at the university. Instead, in the yard behind his home, the professor had built a set of chicken coops. And on his kitchen table he had carefully removed the testicles of four cockerels.

Farmers had been performing this simple procedure for countless generations—caponizing their surplus young roosters so that they would grow plump and tender and bring an even higher price than chickens when sent to market. But Professor Berthold was not interested in improving the quality of capon meat. His purpose was to find out, if possible, *how* the sex glands of a rooster worked, *how* they made him the cocky, strutting, hen-chasing king of the roost.

Thus Berthold did not stop with merely removing the gonads of his four cockerels. He pinioned two of his birds to the table and cut an inch-long incision in the abdomen of each. Then he inserted a single testicle into this unnatural location in each bird, sutured the small wound . . . and waited . . . and watched.

Back in the chicken run the two ordinary capons grew fat and lazy; their combs shrank and lost their brilliant, bloody coloring, and they showed no interest at all in the hens that surrounded them. But the two birds with the transplanted testicles seemed to have no inkling that they had been converted into eunuchs. They flaunted their bright red combs and wattles, which kept growing as if their owners had never been castrated. They battled with the other cocks. Their deep-throated crowing woke the neighbors. And they chased and mounted the hens with all the demonic energy of true roosters.

Then Berthold went one step further. He killed his two rooster-like capons, reopened their abdomens, and carefully examined the glands he had implanted in them. He could find not the slightest sign of nerve regeneration. But he did find that a host of capillaries had developed between the transplanted testicles and the roosters' abdominal walls. Thus the professor concluded that "The testes act *upon the blood* and the blood acts correspondingly *upon the entire organism.*" In other words, the testes produce some sort of substance—what today we would call a hormone—which passes into the bloodstream and travels to a series of target organs upon which it exerts its characteristic controlling influences.

Like all scientists, of course, Berthold did not work in an intellectual vacuum. The idea that maleness and femaleness —and many other physical and mental characteristics— are determined by substances produced by one or another particular organ, came early into man's speculation about the inner workings of his body. The functions of the testes, in particular, must have been easy to recognize because of their proximity to the male organ of coition. Thus, probably in prehistoric times, herdsmen had discovered the effects of castration in making their male domestic animals more docile and in rendering their meat tastier and more tender. From the Old Testament, and from the inscriptions discovered and deciphered by archeologists, we know that many ancient peoples not only had learned how to transform wild young bulls into tame, hardworking oxen, but had also applied the same practice to their slaves—severing the ducts leading from their testicles, thus rendering them eunuchs whom they could safely leave among their womenfolk.

Early Greek, Roman, and Oriental physicians also knew of the existence of most of the other major glands. But probably because these glands are internal, their ideas of their functions were based almost entirely upon their own imaginations. In the second century A.D., for example, Galen described the thyroid in accurate detail but ascribed to it only the fancied duty of providing a lubricating fluid for the larynx. He referred to the ovaries as the *testes muliebres,* or woman's testicles, but he believed that they produced only a fluid which irrigated the uterus to make a fertile soil in which a male seed might take root and grow. He regarded the purpose of the pituitary gland as gathering up waste products of the brain and excreting them into the throat. And he thought of the pancreas—whose Greek name means all flesh—as merely a firm, meaty support for adjacent abdominal structures.

Nor was Galen the last to put forth such misconceptions. Throughout the Middle Ages and right into modern times, many another eminent and respected authority seriously propounded equally fanciful notions. During the late seventeenth century, for example, Dr. Thomas W. Wharton of London was the greatest authority of his day on the anatomy of the glands and the man who gave the thyroid its name—after *thyreos,* the Greek word for shield. Yet he thought of this gland as fulfilling only a cosmetic function. "It contributes much to the rotundity and beauty of the neck," he wrote, "particularly in females, to whom for this reason a larger gland has been assigned, which renders their necks more even and beautiful." Half a century later, Antonio Maria Valsalva, Professor of Anatomy at the University of Bologna, flatly declared that the adrenal glands were the key organs of reproduction, and he described long ducts—now known to be nonexistent—leading from the adrenals to the testes in the male and to the ovaries in the female.

Yet despite the widespread persistence of these misconceptions, in some cases until recent decades, many a physician had at least some intimation that one or another of the body's glands did produce some chemical something which exercised an influence upon distant organs. Thus Frederik Ruysch, a celebrated anatomist of Amsterdam, disagreed with Wharton and suggested, in 1690, that the thyroid poured important substances into the bloodstream. Théophile de Bordeu, physician to Louis XV of France, went much further. In 1776 he wrote: "Each gland . . . is the workshop of a specific substance which passes into the blood, and upon whose secretions the physiological integration of the body as a whole depends."

But such statements—by Ruysch, Bordeu, and a number of others—were themselves merely speculative assertions; a few right guesses amid a host of infinitely varied wrong guesses. Not until our obscure zoölogy professor, Berthold, came along did anyone bother to put such hypotheses to the crucial test of a scientific experiment.

Late in 1848, Berthold wrote a detailed description of his work with capons which was published in the *Archives of Anatomy, Physiology, and Medical Science* under the not very informative title, "Transplantation of Testicles." After that, the professor continued his laboratory work, and wrote and published scores of scientific reports during the remaining twelve years of his life. But, curiously, not one of these research projects had any connection with the fundamental discovery he had made in his backyard chicken run. It was as if Columbus had returned from his discovery of the New World and then spent the rest of his days exploring the side streets of Madrid.

Just why he failed to follow up so promising a beginning, no one knows. Perhaps the faculty and students of Göttingen did ridicule his monkeying about with sex glands, as he had feared they might. Or possibly, he did not quite realize that his first, beautifully simple experiment had clearly marked a path into a new, vast, wide-open field of science.

Tragically, no one else realized it either. Berthold's one short article on the transplantation of testes was completely overlooked until 1910 when Dr. Artur Biedl of Vienna published the first comprehensive treatise on the glands and their hormones. Thus the development of endocrinology was held back for more than sixty years while other researchers struggled painfully, step by step, toward a rediscovery of the basic principal of glandular action—that is, hormones transported through the bloodstream—which Berthold had demonstrated so thoroughly in 1848.

The first of these bit-by-bit advances was scored by Dr. Thomas Addison, the dominant figure for more than four decades at London's famed Guy's Hospital. A master diagnostician, Addison marched daily through the vast wards, "proud and pompous as a parish beadle in his robes of office," with a swarm of awe-struck students in his wake. In grandiloquent sentences, intoned as if he were uttering the Sermon on the Mount, he displayed to them his fantastic memory for all the subtle, minor symptoms by which one disease could be differentiated from another. And it was this memory which led him to the discovery of the rare glandular disease which bears his name.

Early in the 1850s Addison had a patient who, inexplicably, grew more and more emaciated and who finally died despite all his ministrations. The man's relatives removed his body from the hospital and buried him. But within the superb computer that served Addison as a brain, this patient's unprecedented symptoms were permanently encoded—increasing anemia, feebleness of the heart, gastric irritability, and a slight "smoky" or bronzed pigmentation of portions of the skin. Then Addison waited until another patient came along with exactly the same set of symptoms. Again, all treatments failed and the patient gradually succumbed. But this time Addison insisted upon performing an autopsy. And when he cut into the man's emaciated, tanned body he found every organ seemingly normal, save for the little adrenal glands that lie above the kidneys. These were withered and shrunken into tiny fibrous beads.

The great Guy's doctor was quick to realize that he had not only identified a previously unrecognized disease, but had also found its cause. But he was no man to go off half-cocked and announce conclusions based upon a single case. He waited, for more than five years, until eleven such wasting-away patients had turned up at Guy's, died their inevitable deaths, and been found at autopsy to have suffered the identical destruction of their adrenal glands.

Until then no one had known what functions these bits of tissue served nor even whether they served any function at all. But here was clear-cut proof that the adrenals, despite their tiny size, were essential to life—that they somehow helped maintain the normal functioning of the heart and the digestive organs, the blood and the skin, and played a vital role in the growth and maintenance of fatty and muscular tissue. In 1855, with evidence enough to prove his point beyond any challenge, Addison published his monograph "On the Constitutional and Local Effects of Disease of the Supra-Renal Capsules," still highly regarded among medical classics.

In it the cautious doctor made no pretense of knowing *how* the adrenals exercised their tremendous power over so many organs. He was no man for guessing. Instead, he left it to later researchers to conduct the complex studies, on animals and on humans, that were eventually destined to wring almost all the mystery from the adrenals and their hormones. A wise man, Addison. For the adrenals ultimately were found to produce not one but more than forty-five hormones. Over the last eleven decades literally thousands of chemists, physiologists, and physicians have devoted countless years of toil to the vast task of identifying, isolating, and learning how to use the family of adrenal hormones for man's benefit.

In Paris in that same year, 1855, another step toward an understanding of hormone action was taken, this time the result of one of those accidents which now and then lead a truly gifted researcher onto the high road to a major scientific discovery. But then, Dr. Claude Bernard had a unique faculty for incurring such "accidents"—and benefitting science by them. In fact, even his entry into scientific research was more a matter of chance than plan.

Bernard started his working life as a boy assistant in a small-town druggist's shop where he swept the floors, dusted the shelves, ran errands, and occasionally, when his boss was rushed, was allowed to mix one or two of the simpler prescriptions. But such rush periods were few and the lad often had nothing to do during the long evening hours before the lamps were extinguished and the shop closed for the night. Thus, bored, young Claude composed a vaudeville skit, *La Rose du Rhône*, which he offered to the manager of the local theater. When audiences laughed and applauded, he went on to write a five-act drama, *Arthur de Bretagne*; finally abandoning all thought of pharmacy, he headed for Paris and a career as a playwright. There the youth sought out the leading critic, Saint-Marc Girardin. History has not recorded what this worthy thought of the play; but he did have the good sense to ask the budding author how he expected to support himself until producers recognized his talents and the royalties rolled in. When Bernard confessed that he had no private means, Girardin said, "You've learned a little pharmacy. Why not study medicine so that you can make a living and write plays on the side?"

Most stage-struck youngsters would have construed this advice as a callous brushoff. But Claude Bernard took it seriously, enrolled at the Sorbonne, and got a job as a part-time teacher in a girls' school to earn his tuition fees and pay for his food and lodging. By 1843, when he won his medical degree, he had given up both his literary ambitions and his desire to practice medicine, because one of his professors, the physiologist François Magendie, had taken him on as a *préparateur* or lab assistant, taught him how to plan and conduct experiments, and even confessed, "Bernard, you're better at research than I am."

Throughout his thirty-five years as a physiologist, Bernard's interest centered about the metabolic processes by which the body breaks down foods and then rebuilds them into body tissues. It was he who proved that the pancreas was no mere prop to hold kidneys and stomach in position. Through a long series of experiments he demonstrated how this gland produced a pancreatic "juice" which digested proteins, rendered fats absorbable, and converted starches into sugar.

Then Bernard went on to investigate the functions of the liver. In order to compensate for inaccuracies in measurement, he had developed the habit of conducting all of his experiments in duplicate. One day in 1855, while he was studying an extract from a dog's liver, he was called away after his analysis of the first sample, made immedi-

ately after the animal's death. When he analyzed the
second sample, the next day, he was amazed to find that it
contained more sugar than the first. By accident Bernard's
attention had been focused upon a phenomenon he might
otherwise never have observed.

Now he removed the liver from yet another animal and
flushed water through it for nearly an hour until no sugar
could be found in its washings and none could be detected
in the liver tissue. Then he deliberately allowed this sugar-
free liver to stand overnight. Analysis, the next morning,
revealed an abundance of sugar both in the fluid from the
liver and in the liver tissue. The conclusion was inevitable:
since this liver had no blood supply to bring it sugar, there
must exist some sugar-forming substance secreted by the
liver itself. He did not yet know what this substance was.
But to describe it he coined the term "internal secretion."

Bernard crystallized, with these two simple words, a
whole series of vague concepts that had been puzzling
scores of other researchers. For now they could describe
to themselves and to others the functioning not only of
the liver but of other glands as well: by secreting within
themselves active and powerful substances capable of performing a host of chemical transformations within the
body.

Two years later Bernard succeeded in isolating the
liver's internal secretion, which he named glycogen. Later
he showed that both the thyroid and the adrenals similarly
produced internal secretions. Still later others demonstrated that the parathyroid, the ovaries, the testes, the
pituitary, and the thymus glands also produced internal
secretions. They adopted the term endocrine to describe
(in the gobbledegook Greek that scientists love) this family of organs which Bernard described far more simply

as glands of internal secretion. Medical historians have even taken to calling Bernard "the father of endocrinology." Somehow, one can't help wondering whether this modest man, whose life was devoted to simplifying the complex and clarifying the obscure, would really feel honored by so pompous a title as "father" and so unclarifying a word as "endocrinology."

Claude Bernard's contributions to science—unlike poor Berthold's discovery—did not have to await recognition until long after his death. Louis Napoleon built a special laboratory at the natural history museum, the Jardin des Plantes, for the exclusive use of Bernard and his students. A special professorship was established for him; he was elected to the Academy of Medicine, named one of the forty immortals of the French Academy, and created a Senator by imperial decree. When he died in 1878 he was accorded an honor never before bestowed by France upon any man of science—a public funeral. And for at least a generation after his death the seventeen volumes of his published papers served as the bible for all the scientists and physicians who had embarked upon internal secretion research under Bernard's influence.

It was one of the most brilliant of these scientists—and Bernard's successor in the Chair of Experimental Medicine at the Sorbonne—who was fated to bring the still infant science of endocrinology into a disrepute which delayed its development for more than a generation. Charles Édouard Brown-Séquard was born on the island of Mauritius, the son of an American sea captain and a Frenchwoman. As a young man who spoke English and French with equal facility, he practiced medicine in Mauritius, London, and New York. He delivered lectures in Philadelphia, Boston, and Dublin, and served for a time as a professor of physi-

ology at the Medical College of Virginia. Then, early in
the 1850s, he settled down at last, in Paris, and began the
long series of studies of the internal secretions of the
thyroid, the adrenals, the testes, and the pituitary which
earned him a reputation second only to Bernard's.

But Brown-Séquard lacked both Addison's scientific
caution and Bernard's masterly skill in designing foolproof
experiments. Instead of going only as far as facts would
carry him, he tended to postulate a conclusion and then
to warp his experiments—possibly unconsciously—so that
they "proved" what he wanted them to.

In 1869 he suggested that the injection of semen into the
blood of old men might stimulate their mental and physical
powers. He was content, at that time, merely to voice the
suggestion as a sort of inner-circle, scientific jest. But as
he grew older, the idea of rejuvenation fascinated him and
ultimately came to dominate his thinking. In 1875 he attempted a series of testicular grafts on guinea pigs. Fourteen years later, at age seventy-two, he astonished the
world—and alarmed the scientific community—with a
calm announcement that he had rejuvenated himself with
injections of a saline extract of dogs' testicles. "Everything
I have not been able to do for several years on account of
my advanced age," he asserted, "I am, today, able to perform most admirably."

It was long before the days of trained science reporters,
and the journalists who flocked to Brown-Séquard's door
accepted every assertion the old man made as gospel. They
could hardly be blamed for their credulity, for there was a
youthful fire in his aging eyes and he spoke with vigor
and obvious sincerity. Thus the great news—that Brown-
Séquard had discovered a chemical fountain of youth—
was tapped out over the telegraph wires and printed under

large black headlines all over the world. Soon a small army of aged men began heading for Paris in the hope that Brown-Séquard—Ponce de León reborn—would inject their tired veins with his magic elixir and restore to them their youthful vigor and perhaps even sexual prowess.

Most of these pilgrims arrived too late to find any evidence of Brown-Séquard's psychological "rejuvenation"— for that was all it was. Believing in the efficacy of his extract, the old man had stood a little straighter, stayed awake a little longer, walked a bit more firmly than before. But even the psychological stimulus of his faith in himself lasted only about a month. After that, he withered back into senility.

Today, with the wisdom of hindsight, it is easy to see where Brown-Séquard went wrong. Without any experimental evidence—for remember, he did not even know of Berthold's work with capons—he had jumped to the conclusion that the male sex glands secreted some substance that controlled not only sexual vigor but many other bodily functions. Then, again without adequate evidence, he had concluded that this substance was stored in the testicles rather than merely produced in them and distributed promptly into the bloodstream. Thus, to Brown-Séquard, it seemed that all he had to do was to extract this powerful secretion from animal testicles. But here again he went wrong. We know now that his method of saline extraction was incapable of separating the male hormone from testes tissues. Finally, Brown-Séquard had skipped the essential intermediate step of animal experimentation. Instead of testing the potency of his extract upon rabbits or guinea pigs or dogs, he had merely assumed its potency and used it to play a hoax on himself.

When nature exposed that hoax, all too many of the old

man's colleagues in science rushed in to denounce him as a charlatan and a quack. At Parisian soirées, some winked and leered at each other and made him the butt of ribald jokes. Others thundered to their students that all efforts to put extracts from the male gonads to any medical use were doomed to failure.

Thus, disastrous as the incident was for Brown-Séquard, it proved even more disastrous for the nascent science of endocrinology. Men who had been encouraged by the example of Addison and Claude Bernard to take up the study of internal secretions, now felt constrained to channel their work into other, more respectable areas of research. Gifted young clinicians and physiologists were dissuaded from entering the field. For a full generation only a corporal's guard of researchers remained quietly to carry on the endocrine studies which, but for Brown-Séquard, hundreds of bright minds would have been pursuing with enthusiasm and vigor. But these few, during the 1890s, came forth with a series of startling discoveries that put endocrine research back onto the high road.

In 1873 Sir William Withey Gull had observed among some women patients at Guy's Hospital a condition characterized by a dimming of the mental faculties, some loss of memory, and a marked lowering of the basal metabolic rate evidenced by low body temperature and sensitivity to cold. The hair of these women tended to become dry and fall out, and the skin of their faces, arms, and legs grew puffy and swollen. Dr. Gull had no idea of what caused this condition. But in 1888 another London physician, Sir Victor Horsley, demonstrated conclusively, by experimentally removing the thyroids of monkeys and other animals that myxedema—as it had come to be called—was due to a loss of function of the thyroid gland.

By 1891, only two years after the Brown-Séquard fiasco, Dr. George Redmayne Murray, Professor of Comparative Pathology at the University of Durham, had prepared a glycerine extract of sheep's thyroid which he injected into a forty-six-year-old victim of severe myxedema. Under six months of such treatment, the woman achieved a complete recovery which was maintained by additional, periodic injections of thyroid extract until her death—from other causes—at age seventy-four. This marked the first instance of the successful treatment of a glandular-deficiency disease by replacement therapy. Within a year British physicians had discovered that thyroid extracts were effective even when given by mouth. Since then—using this method of supplying to the body a hormone it cannot produce in adequate quantities—physicians have relieved the suffering of millions of victims of thyroid deficiency.

Meanwhile at London's University College, two physiologists, Edward A. Schafer and George Oliver, had joined forces to study the adrenal glands. From animals sacrificed by other researchers, they had obtained a number of these tiny tissues, ground them up, and produced a thimbleful of crude extract. When they injected a bit of this into a laboratory dog, they noted a marked and almost instant soaring of its blood pressure, what they called a pressor effect to distinguish it from a *de*pressor effect.

But Schafer and Oliver knew that the adrenals had a double structure, with an outer bark, or cortex, surrounding an inner core, or marrow, called the medulla. Thus they now went on to refine their experiment. First they brewed an extract of the cortex and tested that on dogs. The results: utterly negative. Then they followed the same procedure using only adrenal medullae. And this time, when they injected their new extract into dogs, blood pressure shot up more rapidly than before and to an even higher level.

Here it seemed was the explanation of at least one part of the puzzle of Addison's disease. The unusually *low* blood pressure of all its victims was due to failure of their wasted adrenals to produce this pressor substance. Here too was at least a partial explanation of how our bodies are able to mobilize themselves for intensive action in a crisis, by calling forth a surge of the pressor substance to stimulate the beating of the heart so that, almost instantly, it may send to the muscles and the brain an increased flow of oxygen-carrying blood.

Schafer and Oliver published their findings in 1894. Immediately, chemists and physiologists all over this world set out to discover the exact nature of this pressor substance. By 1901 both J. J. Abel and the Japanese researcher Jokichi Takamine had isolated it in crystalline form. By 1904 the German chemist Frederich Stolz had worked out a way of synthesizing this hormone from common chemicals. Thus doctors no longer had to rely upon crude and expensive extracts. With the synthetic, which had been named adrenaline, they could often restart a stopped heart, quickly relieve an acute attack of bronchial asthma, or temporarily constrict the peripheral capillaries and thus help stop hemorrhages.

It was, however, two other University College physiologists, William Maddock Bayliss and Ernest Henry Starling, who transformed the study of internal secretions from a series of random investigations into a unified branch of science. They started, at the turn of the century, by reperforming an experiment that Russia's famed physiologist Ivan Pavlov had performed a year or two earlier. Studying the processes of digestion, Pavlov had discovered that the pancreas began pouring forth its digestive juices as soon as the first bit of half-digested food emerged from the stomach and entered the upper part of the small intestine. He had noted that in the stomach, food becomes strongly acidified. And he had assumed, therefore, that this acid, upon entering the normally alkaline intestine, activated nerves which signaled the pancreas to get on with its job and send its juices into the intestine.

But Bayliss and Starling were not quite willing to accept this idea of a nerve signal on assumption alone. Instead, they designed a sub-experiment that would prove— or disprove—it. On a series of laboratory animals, they severed all the nerves reaching the upper intestine and then introduced into this organ an acid porridge simulating food as it normally emerges from the stomach. If Pavlov's assumption was correct, the pancreas would receive no signal because the nerves were cut; the telegraph wires were down. But every time they tried this test they found, to their surprise, that the pancreatic juices poured promptly into the intestine. Clearly, Pavlov's assumption was wrong.

But if it was not a nerve signal that touched off pancreatic activity, could it be some chemical secreted by the lining of the intestine? To test that assumption, the two researchers stripped off the mucous lining of an upper intestine, ground it up fine, added dilute hydrochloric acid, and injected this mixture into the vein of a laboratory animal. As soon as its blood had carried the injection to the pancreas, that gland sprang into activity. Bayliss and Starling therefore concluded that in the presence of acid, the mucous cells lining the upper intestine walls secreted a chemical substance which "told" the pancreas to set its juices flowing.

They named their new-found secretion secretin. It not

only stimulated the pancreas into activity, it also stimulated its discoverers into reviewing the work of Addison, Bernard, Brown-Séquard, Gull, Horsley, Murray, Schafer, Oliver, and others who had studied one or another of the internal secretions. From this study they developed a new picture of the endocrine glands. They saw them not as isolated organs, but as an *integrated system* which responds to the changing needs of the body by producing a wide range of chemical messengers, to be carried by the blood to target tissues where they stimulate or depress a host of tissue activities. To describe these blood-borne chemical stimulators Starling coined the word hormone, from the Greek *hormao*, "I arouse to activity."

Viewed in this light, the endocrine glands and their hormones constituted a second communication system within the body, the first—of course—being the nervous system. Later researchers have shown that in evolutionary terms, it is by far the older of the two systems; for plants produce hormones although they have no nerves. Other investigators have discovered that in man and all the higher animals, the nerve and hormone systems operate not wholly independently, but are closely interlinked at many points. Nerve activity may trigger the hormone system into operation and hormones may evoke nervous activity.

That Starling and Bayliss, in the early 1900s, did not appreciate all of these and other fine points in no way diminishes the epochal significance of their vision of the endocrine-hormone system. It brought order where previously there had been chaos. And it set into motion the great and infinitely productive expansion of hormone research which has continued to this day.

2

•

THE EXTRACT ERA

•

Unlike the sensational rejuvenation claims of Brown-Séquard, the work of Bayliss and Starling evoked no interest from the public press. But among medical and scientific research workers, their clarifying theory of hormone action had an electrifying effect. Almost overnight endocrinology ceased to be the Cinderella of medicine and began to command the intense interest of many of its brightest minds.

Medical school professors and their students avidly read and earnestly discussed every word the two British scientists published. All over the world alert and perceptive physicians began to observe their patients more closely for any signs that seemed to link any abnormal condition to a malfunctioning of one or another of the endocrine glands. In autopsy rooms pathologists, who previously had tended to ignore these tiny tissues, now carefully dissected them. Whenever they found some abnormality in an endocrine gland they checked the records to see if it tied in with symptoms noted by the attending physicians before the patient's death. And in scores of laboratories physiologists and biochemists initiated ever widening efforts to explore the functioning of all the endocrine glands and, hopefully, to make the hormones these glands produced available for use in the treatment of disorders arising from glandular deficiencies.

Inevitably, many of these projects led down blind alleys. Many others produced bits of new knowledge of potential value only to later researchers. But, slowly at first and then with increasing frequency, breakthroughs of direct value in the treatment of the ailing were scored.

In 1909, for example, the British pharmacologist Henry Hallett Dale developed an extract of the posterior pituitary gland which obstetricians found extremely useful in stimulating uterine contractions in cases of difficult labor, and enabling them to save the lives of both mothers and babies.

Two years later the French physiologist Albert Pézard prepared the first effective extract of testicular tissue and proved its hormonal properties by using it to stimulate the growth of capons' combs. Pézard's extract was too crude to be useful in the treatment of human ills, but his capon-comb test provided a valuable method by which later researchers could quickly assay their testicular extracts to determine their power to exert male hormone activity. And in 1913 Henri Iscovesco, a Roumanian physiologist working in

France, succeeded in developing a demonstrably active extract of ovarian tissue, thus laying the basis for more successful efforts by other scientists, to isolate the female sex hormones.

Since 1891 physicians had been using glycerine extracts of sheep thyroids in the treatment of human thyroid deficiency diseases. But at the Mayo Clinic in Rochester, Minnesota, a young biochemist, Edward Kendall, was convinced that a purer, more powerful thyroid extract could be prepared. In 1914 he succeeded in refining his extracts all the way down to crystalline form, thus isolating the pure thyroid hormone itself. Kendall's thyroxin did not completely replace the less expensive crude thyroid extracts. But it provided physicians with an extremely active substance of special value in the relief of certain severe thyroid dysfunctions.

Of all mankind's afflictions, few have been more common and more deadly than the hormone deficiency disease diabetes mellitus. At least two thousand years ago Greek physicians had learned to recognize its major symptoms: a wasting away of the flesh despite a raging thirst and a ravenous appetite, and, as the word diabetes indicates, a siphoning off of abnormally great quantities of urine. In the mid-1600s the brilliant British physician Thomas Willis provided his colleagues with an even more definite method of reaching an early diagnosis: "Taste thy patient's urine," he told them. "If it be sweet like honey, he will waste away, grow weak, fall into sleep, and die."

Two centuries later another British physician, Dr. Richard Bright, noted at the autopsy table that the pancreatic glands of patients who had died of diabetes often contained numerous small crystals, or calculi. This observation, later confirmed by many other pathologists, clearly implicated the pancreas as somehow involved with the disease. And in 1889, in Germany, Drs. Joseph von Mering and Oskar Minkowski devised the crucial experiment that proved this association.

They removed a healthy dog's pancreas. The next day, flies clustered around the sweet-smelling urine the animal had excreted in its cage. From then on the dog evinced all the symptoms of diabetes long recognized in humans. Sugar levels in his blood soared. Although his diet was increased, his muscles and fatty tissues wasted away. Within a few weeks, weighing less than half as much as before his operation, the animal fell into a coma and died.

But could it have been the loss of the digestive juices from his pancreas that had caused his sickness and death? To answer this question, a less drastic operation was tried. Instead of excising a dog's entire pancreas, the experimenters simply tied off the ducts that carried its juices to his intestines. In the days that followed the dog showed no sign of diabetes. Although his pancreas could no longer send forth digestive juices, it was obviously still producing another secretion; some unknown anti-diabetic substance was passing not through the closed-off ducts but directly into the bloodstream.

Decades earlier the physiologist Paul Langerhans had described small but distinct units of tissue, many thousands of which he had found scattered throughout all the pancreatic glands he had dissected. Thus attention became centered upon these islets of Langerhans as the possible source of a diabetes-preventing secretion. And in 1901 Dr. Eugene Lindsay Opie of The Johns Hopkins Hospital confirmed this suspicion by showing that in many cases of diabetes, these islets had partly or completely degenerated.

When the Bayliss-Starling concept of hormone action won wide acceptance, many a researcher had realized that diabetes was indeed the result of a hormone deficiency and had tried, therefore, to extract and isolate the active substance produced by Langerhans' islets. Until 1921, however, all of these attempts had failed. No matter how the hormone-hunters varied their methods of extraction, the extracts they produced proved powerless.

But in that year a twenty-nine-year-old orthopedic surgeon, Dr. Frederick G. Banting, abandoned his poor practice in London, Ontario. Selling his books and instruments, he traveled to the University of Toronto determined to achieve what so many before him had failed to accomplish. There, Professor John J. R. Macleod, who was leaving for an extended vacation in Europe, gave him permission to use his physiology laboratory during his absence and supplied him with ten lab dogs. Almost as an afterthought Dr. Macleod instructed his twenty-two-year-old assistant, a second-year medical student named Charles A. Best, to do what he could to help Dr. Banting.

On May 16, they started to work. It was Banting's belief that earlier researchers had failed because when they ground up their pancreatic glands, the digestive juices had inactivated the hormone of the islets of Langerhans. To surmount this obstacle he tied off the pancreatic ducts of several of his dogs, hoping that the cells which secreted the digestive juices would degenerate more quickly than the islet cells. After a series of failures the two young partners in research finally obtained one thoroughly shriveled pancreas, which, when cut open, revealed islets still intact. They sliced this gland, froze it, thawed it, ground it up, and filtered the resulting mash.

Then Banting injected a few cubic centimeters of this

extract into a diabetic dog . . . and both men waited. Before this injection a test had revealed a dangerously high blood-sugar level in the almost comatose animal, already too weak to lift its head. But an hour later, when they drew a few droplets of blood from the dog's paw and performed a second blood test, the sugar level was down. It was lower still on the next test and close to normal on the test after that. The animal, glassy-eyed and half dead just a few hours before, now sat up, wagged its tail and joyfully hailed his young benefactors with a tentative but distinctly audible bark.

But soon Banting and Best found that it took all the hormone they could extract from a single pancreas to keep just one diabetic dog alive for less than two days. Unless they could find some source of great quantities of hormone-rich pancreas glands, their discovery would be useless. Then Fred Banting remembered reading that in unborn animals the pancreas consisted almost entirely of islet cells, because there was no need for digestive juices in the womb. He knew, too, that farmers often deliberately bred cows to increase their weight before they were sent to slaughter. Thus, from a local slaughterhouse, he and Best obtained many pounds of such immature pancreatic glands. And when they harvested their extracts, they had enough hormone to keep all their remaining diabetic dogs alive and healthy indefinitely.

But would insulin—as they were now calling their hormone extract—work just as well on human diabetics? And was it, in fact, safe to use? Banting rolled up his sleeve and directed Best to inject a dose of the extract into him. Then, without waiting to see what would happen to his friend, Best bared his arm and commanded Banting to give him a shot. The next day, save for slightly sore arms, they were none the worse for their experiment.

Reassured, they crossed the street to the Toronto General Hospital, where a fourteen-year-old boy had wasted away to less than seventy pounds. Into the dying lad's pitifully thin arm they administered an insulin injection—and, just as it had happened with their dogs, his blood-sugar level dropped. With each subsequent injection the boy improved. Within a few days he was able to get out of bed. Within a few weeks he returned to his home, still dependent, of course, upon insulin injections but otherwise in perfect health. He was the first of the scores of millions whose lives have since been saved by insulin.

Now honors were showered upon Dr. Banting. The Canadian Parliament voted him a life annuity, and the University named a new research institute after him. In 1923 the Nobel Prize for Medicine was awarded to Banting and to Professor Macleod, who had worked on the standardization of insulin after its discovery. But at this point Dr. Banting could no longer contain his indignation at the neglect of Charles Best. To call to the attention of all the world that insulin was their joint discovery, he publicly shared half his prize with the man who had shared all his work and all his worries during that long hot summer in which insulin was born.

With the triumphant isolation of insulin, hormone-hunters, here and in Europe, were emboldened to renew an old drive—their search for the internal secretions that control the growth and the functioning of the reproductive organs and the development of all the secondary sex characteristics that distinguish males from females. If these hormones could be isolated and made available, endocrinologists felt sure they would prove invaluable in the relief of a host of conditions caused by sex gland malfunction; disorders ranging all the way from disfiguring facial hair growths in women to failures of sexual maturation in males.

With his testicle-transplanting experiment, Berthold had proved the existence of a male sex hormone way back in 1848. In similar fashion, in 1896, a Viennese gynecologist, Dr. Emil Knauer, had proved the existence of a female sex hormone by transplanting ovaries into immature female animals, who quickly displayed mature sex characteristics. Numerous attempts had since been made to extract this female sex hormone from animal ovaries, but the substances early experimenters obtained were crude and of such low potency that endocrinologists found them of virtually no therapeutic value.

Yet there was no doubt that even these crude extracts did contain the putative female hormone. In 1923 Dr. Edgar Allen of Washington University in St. Louis had proved this conclusively by injecting such an ovarian extract into immature female rats. Within forty-eight hours these baby rats came into heat—or estrus—just as if they possessed fully mature ovaries.

But when Dr. Allen and his colleague, biochemist Edward A. Doisy, tried to concentrate more active estrus-stimulating —or estrogenic—extracts from ovaries, they ran into technical difficulties they could not surmount. Then, in 1927, the Berlin gynecologists Drs. Selmar Aschheim and Bernhard Zondek helped solve this problem through a seemingly unrelated discovery. Their search was for a simple means of diagnosing pregnancy in its earliest stages, before it could be detected by direct physical examination. And they found that if they injected a patient's urine into an immature laboratory mouse or rat, they could get an accurate yes-or-no answer. If the patient was not pregnant, the test animal showed no reaction; if the patient was pregnant, the animal displayed an estrus reaction, despite its immaturity. Clearly, with the onset of pregnancy the ovaries' production of hormones soared so high that substantial quantities of active estrogenic substances were excreted in the urine.

As soon as they learned of the Aschheim-Zondek discovery, Drs. Allen and Doisy realized that, in pregnancy urine, they had a rich and far more easily handled source of female hormone from which to develop a potent extract. But they were not alone in this realization. In French, Dutch, and German laboratories others simultaneously recognized the same opportunity. Thus a great race began, to develop the most concentrated possible extract or even to isolate the pure hormone itself.

In the laboratories of the German pharmaceutical firm, Schering-Kahlbaum, chemists reduced gallons and gallons of urine to a few ounces of dark-brown syrup. Tested on mice by the Aschheim-Zondek technique, it displayed an estrogenic effect but by no means as strong a one as they desired. And at this point Schering's chemists got stuck and turned to Professor Adolf Windaus of Göttingen University for help. Windaus, in turn, passed the problem on to his most brilliant assistant, twenty-six-year-old Adolf Butenandt. Both Butenandt and the Allen-Doisy team started this phase of their work late in 1927. For nearly two years they moved ahead, neck and neck. Then, in the fall of 1929, Doisy and Allen were able to announce the isolation of a pure crystal female sex hormone, estrone. Barely two months later Butenandt reached the same goal. By 1931 both Parke, Davis & Co. and Schering-Kahlbaum were able to make the powerful pure hormone available to endocrinologists and clinicians who quickly found a host of therapeutic uses for it.

The Schering-Kahlbaum chemists had turned for aid to Professor Windaus, because they suspected that their gummy extract of pregnancy urine contained steroid substances and Adolf Windaus was the world's foremost expert on this unique group of organic chemicals. Way back in 1903, at the University of Freiburg, he had written his doctoral dissertation on these compounds, which derive their generic name from the Greek *stereos*—meaning solid —because, while they are members of the great alcohol family, they differ from the common alcohols in being subject to crystalline solidification. At Freiburg and later at Göttingen, Windaus had worked out the chemical composition of cholesterol, the sterol of animal bile which, in solid form, is the major constituent of human gallstones. He had gone on to study a host of other, closely related sterols of both animal and plant origin. And he had pioneered in the development of derivatives of digitalis—a plant sterol—and of vitamin D or ergosterol. Perhaps more important for the future of hormone research, he had gathered around himself and trained a small army of young steroid chemists, not only Germans but Swiss, English, French, Japanese, Dutch, and American students who had eagerly competed for the privilege of working under the guidance of this master teacher.

When Windaus began his work chemists could describe cholesterol only by the non-informative formula $C_{27}H_{45}OH$. But, through years of diligent probing, Windaus had worked out the precise molecular structure of cholesterol and of scores of related compounds—an achievement all the more remarkable because he had none of the complex analytical tools that modern chemists take for granted.

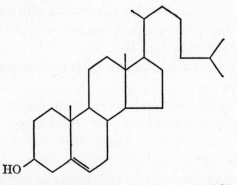

Structural diagram of cholesterol, the "raw material" which our bodies convert into steroid hormones.

All of these steroids had one thing in common: a group of seventeen carbon atoms arranged in four rings. By general agreement, chemists today diagram this steroid nucleus as if it were made of four small bathroom-floor tiles—three of them perfect hexagons and the fourth of pentagon shape, because it is formed by only five carbon atoms. Since one steroid differs from another mainly by the position and the nature of the side chains attached to this basic nucleus, a convention of chemists agreed upon a common system of lettering the rings as A, B, C, and D, and numbering the

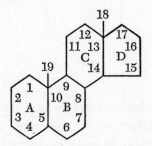

The basic steroid nucleus, a framework of interlinked carbon atoms common to all natural and synthetic steroid hormones.

carbon atoms from one through seventeen in a standardized
order, so that side chain positions can be easily identified in
shorthand chemical formulas. Numbers higher than seventeen are reserved to identify certain common side chain
structures.

When Adolf Butenandt isolated estrone and analyzed its
structure, he discovered that—just as his Schering colleagues
had suspected—this pure crystalline substance was indeed a
steroid, the first of all hormones found to be a member of
this molecular family. It had the classic steroid nucleus. But
in place of the extremely complex cholesterol side chain, at
the 17 position at the top of ring D, it had only a single
oxygen atom linked to the carbon.

To hormone-hunters this discovery suggested a host of
fascinating possibilities. For example, since the male testes
develop from the same type of embryonic cell as do the female ovaries, the strong suspicion was raised that the male

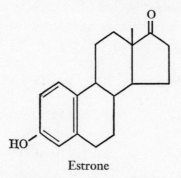

Estrone

hormone would also turn out to be a steroid. Beyond that,
the hormones of other glands might also have steroidal structures. If this hypothesis were correct, it would provide a
shortcut to their isolation and thus hasten their application in
medical therapy. The minds of the more imaginative

hormone-seekers even envisioned another possibility, though one that seemed still far over the horizon. Professor Windaus and his disciples had learned how to manipulate and alter steroid molecules. Thus, some day it might become possible to duplicate natural steroid hormones by chemical synthesis and even to create biologically active steroids that nature itself had not invented. Not even the most optimistic, however, guessed how very soon that "day" was to arrive.

Ideas such as these stimulated hormone-hunters everywhere to redoubled efforts. And with steroid chemists now added to their ranks, new developments poured forth from

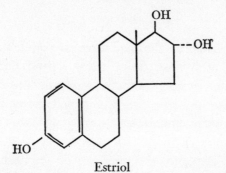

Estriol

research laboratories in an amazing flood. In 1930 Dr. Guy Frederic Marrian of London isolated another estrogenic steroid from pregnancy urine. This substance, estriol (see diagram), differed only slightly from estrone. But these seemingly minor side chain differences gave it a milder activity.

By 1933, in Germany, the steroid chemists Drs. Erwin Schwenk and Fritz Hildebrandt converted estrone into a third form of estrogenic steroid, estradiol, biologically much more active than either of its forerunners. And only two years later Dr. Doisy demonstrated, by extracting estradiol directly from sows' ovaries, that it is actually a natural female hormone. Estrone and estriol appear in pregnancy urine because they are excreted metabolites of estradiol, the active hormone produced in the ovaries.

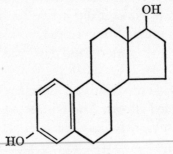

Estradiol

By 1935 physicians thus had three estrogenic substances of therapeutic usefulness. Since then, steroid chemists have created numerous other modified molecules possessing estrogenic activity and thus vastly widened the choice of such drugs available to clinicians.

But were estrogens the only female sex hormones? The cyclic nature of the ovaries' activities long had led physiologists to believe that a second ovarian hormone must exist. As far back as 1903, in fact, Dr. Ludwig Fraenkel at the German University of Breslau had discovered that once the ovaries release an egg, a yellow substance forms within the ruptured egg sac. A few years later French researchers, Drs. Paul Bouin and Albert Ancel, found convincing evidence that this corpus luteum, or yellow body, served the important function of preparing the uterus for pregnancy.

By 1930, building upon this knowledge, Dr. George W. Corner and his student-assistant Willard M. Allen, at the University of Rochester, succeeded in producing a corpus luteum extract. And in 1934 the pure hormone of the corpus luteum was almost simultaneously isolated by Drs. Butenandt and K. H. Slotta, working independently in Germany, by Drs. Willard Allen and Oscar Wintersteiner in the United States, and by Drs. Albert Wettstein and Max Hartmann in Switzerland.

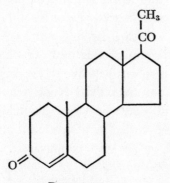

Progesterone

Because it favored the processes of gestation, this second female sex hormone, again a steroid, was called progesterone. Since then—as with the estrogens—steroid chemists have put together a long series of other progestationally active compounds.

Even as the mysteries of the dual female sex hormones were being resolved, other researchers were hot on the trail of the male hormone. Starting in 1926, the University of Chicago's Professor of Physiologic Chemistry Fred C. Koch and his student-assistant Lemuel McGee had ground up bulls' testicles and prepared one extract after another. When they assayed them by the capon-comb test, some displayed a little more male hormone activity than others. But none showed enough activity to be labeled even "promising."

After two years the small grant under which they had worked ran out and was not renewed.

Undaunted, however, Fred Koch spent his own salary to purchase more bulls' testicles and gallons of solvents. And in 1929 he and Dr. T. F. Gallagher finally developed a many-staged extraction process that yielded a mixture much more active than any Koch had ever before been able to prepare. Where it had taken weeks for his old extracts to evoke even a little growth in a capon's withered comb, one hundredth of a milligram of this new substance produced an upstanding red comb in just five days. Anyone less modest or more impetuous than Fred Koch would have shouted "eureka." Instead, when he wrote his deliberately dry and factual report, he ended it with a cautionary declaration. "The product is as yet grossly impure. . . . It should not be given a chemical name."

But Koch's report was not buried and forgotten as old Professor Berthold's had been eighty years earlier. Other researchers recognized it as a challenge and especially so did Adolf Butenandt, fresh from his triumph in the extraction of estrone. By 1931, using urine rather than testicles, Butenandt managed to isolate a few grains of crystalline hormone. Because it stimulated comb growth *and* because it was a steroid, he coined a Greek name for it: androsterone. While it was biologically active, it was soon found to be not the male hormone itself but a metabolically changed or degraded form of the true hormone.

By 1935, however, a team working under the Dutch pharmacologist, Dr. Ernest Laqueur, and using an improved variant of Koch's method, succeeded in extracting the true male hormone from bulls' testicles. Inevitably, it was called testosterone.

Just one year later Leopold Ruzicka, a Yugoslav chemist

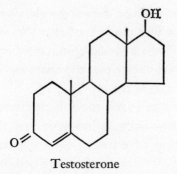

Testosterone

working in Switzerland, managed to change cholesterol into a synthetic duplicate of natural testosterone. The steroid extract era was drawing to its end; the modern period of deliberate steroid hormone synthesis was beginning.

While clinicians were exploring, and rapidly extending, the therapeutic applications of the male and female sex hormones, physiologists were deeply puzzled by a series of related questions. What triggered the output of testosterone in an adolescent boy and thus changed him into a fertile, deep-voiced, beard-growing, muscular man? What triggered the quite different changes of puberty that transformed girls into women? And what "told" the ovaries when to increase estrogen output and when to turn on their production of progesterone?

As far back as 1922 Drs. Herbert McLean Evans and Joseph Abraham Long, at the University of California at Berkeley, had injected extracts of the front, or anterior, half of the pituitary gland into normal female rats. When they did this, they found that the ovaries of these animals produced abnormally large quantities of corpus luteum. Following this lead, a series of researchers gradually worked out the complex interactions between the pituitary, at the base of the brain, and the distant sex glands or gonads. After years of work it was discovered that the anterior pituitary produced two distinct gonad-stimulating hormones, named gonadotropins to indicate that the testes and the ovaries were their particular target tissues.

One of these was called the follicle-stimulating hormone —FSH for short—because it was at first thought to cause only the secretion of estrogen by the ovaries and thus to bring about the maturation of an egg cell in its little follicle or capsule. Later research proved that FSH had other functions. At puberty it stimulates the development of the ovaries and the production of sperm cells.

The second gonadotropic hormone has, confusingly, gone under two names. It was first called the interstitial-cell-stimulating hormone—or ICSH—because it stimulated the secretion of testosterone by the interstitial cells of the testes and thus caused the growth of the male accessory reproductive organs (the penis and the prostate) and the development and maintenance of the secondary characteristics of maleness. But it was later called the lutenizing hormone— LH—because, in females, it triggered the formation of the corpus luteum and brought about ovulation.

Recent research has demonstrated that the interplay between these two gonadotropins is more complex than was originally believed, for the presence of each, in small quantities, seems to be necessary for the other to accomplish its tropic effects. And the pituitary's output of these tropic hormones is, in turn, regulated by a feedback action. In large measure the quantity of testosterone, estrogen, or progesterone carried by the blood to the pituitary "instructs" that master gland when to step up or to reduce its output of either gonadotropic hormone.

Both of these pituitary hormones are made up of large

chain-like protein molecules, each containing hundreds of atoms. Thus, scientists have not yet been able to synthesize them in quantity. For the limited therapeutic uses so far found for these hormones, clinicians have relied upon extracts made from the pituitaries of sheep.

The gonadotropins, however, are not the only hormones produced by the anterior pituitary. Suspended just below the brain, it functions as the body's master gland. Its thyrotropic hormone—TSH—controls the growth and activity of the thyroid gland. Its somatotropic or growth hormone—called either STH or GH—acts upon the whole body, both regulating metabolic processes and stimulating the body's growth and maturation. Its lactogenic hormone—LTH—is, as its name implies, essential for the production of mothers' milk. And its adrenocorticotropic hormone—ACTH—controls the adrenal glands in their production of a host of steroid hormones.

Since the days of Thomas Addison the adrenals had been known to be essential for the maintenance of life. During the 1920s and 1930s numerous researchers developed extracts of the adrenal cortex. And when it was found that the hormones in these extracts were steroids, many of the teams that had worked on the isolation of the sex steroids then turned their attention (as we shall see in chapters 4 and 6) to the isolation of the many adrenocortical steroids and the exploration of their varied functions.

Some corticosteroids were found to be regulators of the body's temperature, the rate of its heartbeat, or the blood pressure. Others affected the blood-sugar level or the liver's secretion of glycogen. The so-called glucosteroids were concerned with carbohydrate metabolism; the mineralocorticoids controlled water-and-salt balance.

In varying degrees, all were found to help in mobilizing the body's defenses against allergies, inflammations, and excessive or prolonged stress. And, as with the pituitary hormones, a whole series of feedback mechanisms were discovered by which the adrenals regulated the activities of other glands and were, in turn, stimulated or depressed in their action by hormones produced by other members of the endocrine gland family.

Until recent years very little had been learned about the other endocrine glands. The parathyroids were not clearly identified as separate from the thyroid, in which they are embedded, until 1880. By 1909 it was found, by Drs. W. G. MacCallum and Carl Voegtlin of The Johns Hopkins University, that tetany—a painful, spastic disease of the bones and muscles—is the result of a calcium deficiency caused in turn by a deficiency of parathyroid secretion. In 1915, at the University of Alberta, a team under Dr. James B. Collip prepared an extract of beef parathyroids which proved of value in the relief of tetany.

At the Rockefeller Institute, Drs. Howard Rasmussen and Lyman C. Craig have been working, since 1957, on methods of purifying this hormone. Pure extracts have been obtained, but only in milligram quantities and at great expense. If and when a mass-production process can be perfected, it may become possible for clinicians to launch a bold attack not only against rare tetany but against a number of other, more common calcium deficiency diseases, such as the bone-weakening condition known to doctors as osteomalacia.

Until the last decade, so little evidence concerning the hormone activity of the minuscule pineal gland was available, that some physiologists refused to dignify it as an endocrine organ at all and deliberately referred to it as the pineal *body*. But recent research has shown that its removal from laboratory rats results in an increase in the size of the ovaries. On the other hand, the injection into rats of a beef pineal extract retards ovarian growth and causes some enlargement of the adrenal and pituitary glands. Other studies, on cattle and humans, have produced some evidence that the pineal secretes a factor called melatonin, which is believed to reverse, in some way yet unknown, the skin-darkening effect of one of the pituitary hormones.

Even these few insights into pineal function have not yet been firmly established as facts. But the case of the thymus gland illustrates how rapidly modern intensive endocrine research *may* change a state of all but total ignorance about a gland's function into one of substantial and fast-growing knowledge.

As late as 1961 virtually nothing was known about the thymus save that, in both humans and animals, it began to atrophy early in life and often left only shreds of scar tissue by the time of sexual maturation. Then at the Chester Beatty Institute in England, Dr. Jacques F. A. P. Miller tried removing the thymus from newborn mice. For several weeks after their thymectomies, the baby mice seemed to thrive. But after that they fell ill, and ultimately died, of a disease marked by rapid weight loss and diarrhea.

Post-mortem examinations revealed an extreme depletion of the lymphocytes, or white blood corpuscles. The thymus apparently secretes a hormone that stimulates the spleen and lymph nodes to produce lymphocytes, the scavenger cells especially concerned with attacking and destroying invading infectious organisms. Thus, in the absence of the thymus, the mice became easy prey to infections they would ordinarily have been able to resist.

Present theory postulates that the thymus' hormone is essential only until antibody-forming mechanisms take over the main task of fighting foreign invading bodies. At that point—in humans, the period just before puberty—the no longer needed gland fades away and is reabsorbed.

The actual thymus hormone has yet to be identified and then, hopefully, to be extracted or synthesized for therapeutic use. If the hormone is indeed, as now seems possible, the trigger to the development of immunity processes in our bodies, clinicians will undoubtedly find innumerable uses for it; possibly in inducing skin grafts and other transplanted tissues to "take," in fighting allergies, or in bolstering the immunity of those children whose apparent proneness to infection may be due to some underfunctioning of their thymus glands.

Today such ideas are mere speculations. But the whole history of endocrine research is replete with instances in which similar, highly speculative prospects for the relief of major ailments have been fulfilled—often far sooner than those who had envisioned them had dared to hope.

3

•

_____

FROM MICROGRAMS
TO MASS PRODUCTION

_____

•

By the early 1940s the medical usefulness of the sex steroids was no longer in question. Week after week leading medical journals were publishing the reports of distinguished clinical research teams which had developed one or another new use for testosterone, the estrogens, or progesterone. All over the world obstetricians, gynecologists, cancer specialists, and general practitioners were anxious to prescribe the new, more effective extracts and the even newer "pure" compounds for their patients.

But in tens of thousands of cases the astronomically high cost of sex hormones made such prescription prohibitive. Progesterone, for example, appeared able to prevent a large portion of all miscarriages among so-called "habitual aborters"—women who failed to secrete enough natural corpus luteum to maintain a pregnancy. To be an effective substitute, however, repeated substantial doses of progesterone had to be injected, or implanted as subcutaneous pellets, throughout the first four or five months of pregnancy. And at $200 a gram, only the wealthiest could possibly afford to pay for such treatment.

In part, the high cost of sex hormones was the direct result of the complex and elaborate methods by which they had to be produced. To secure barely enough androsterone to cover the head of a pin, Adolph Butenandt had had to start with nearly four thousand gallons of urine; to obtain less than one hundredth of an ounce of pure testosterone crystals, Ernst Laqueur had had to process nearly a ton of bulls' testicles. It took a full ton of cholesterol, from the spinal cords or brains of cattle or from the grease of sheep's wool, to yield just twenty pounds of the starting material from which progesterone ultimately could be obtained. Dr. Edward Doisy had had to process the ovaries of more than eighty thousand sows to get just twelve thousandths of a gram of estradiol.

Chemists were, of course, improving their hormone producing techniques. Yields were beginning to rise, and the cost of manufacture was dropping. But many of the key process patents were owned by European companies who used them to maintain high prices throughout the world. Thus, no matter how much the steroid hormones might help them, millions of potential users had to do without.

The man who broke this vicious bottleneck was a

maverick genius named Russell Marker. He was born in Hagerstown, Maryland, in 1902, the year in which Starling and Bayliss had laid the basis for all modern hormone research. Even as a youngster he seemed different somehow from the other small-town boys; while they played baseball or football or went fishing, he haunted the Hagerstown library to bury his nose in its small collection of technical books. His high school record was undistinguished save in chemistry, the one subject in which he quickly learned everything his instructors could teach him and then rushed far beyond all that they knew. And when he went to the University of Maryland he spent his days and nights in the organic chemistry labs.

Marker got a B.S. in organic chemistry in 1923 and with it a fellowship for advanced studies. But the restlessness that was to characterize the remainder of his life was already apparent. At the end of two years, although he had completed his work for his doctorate, he became involved in a disagreement with one of his professors and left the university without obtaining his advanced degree. He went to work, instead, in the laboratories of a petrochemical company.

In 1928 he quit that job and headed for the Rockefeller Institute for Medical Research where Dr. P. A. Levene was quick to recognize the young man's extraordinary talents. But the year's budget was already set and there was no money with which to hire him. Rather than turn him away, however, Dr. Levene managed to "bootleg" him onto the staff, paying him a pocket-money stipend out of the funds allotted for the purchase of chemical reagents. And here, despite his lack of status or adequate salary, Russell Marker was in a personal heaven. In his corner of the laboratory he was free to do the one thing he wanted to do: to lock himself in—sometimes for days on end—while he rigged up apparatus and concocted compounds that no one else had yet succeeded in putting together. Together with Levene, he co-authored no fewer than twenty-six papers on the chemical configurations of organic compounds.

For nearly six years Marker worked at his dream job. Then, one day, after what others thought of as a minor disagreement with one of his fellow organic chemists, the young man stalked out of the Institute and never came back.

By that time, however, he had a growing reputation as a chemist particularly gifted in devising efficient, high-yield processes for breaking down complex organic materials and recombining them into new, pure crystalline substances. Thus he had no trouble in obtaining an appointment, in 1935, as Professor of Organic Chemistry at Pennsylvania State College. And shortly after he went there, Parke, Davis & Co.—anxious to expand its position in the budding hormone field—began to subsidize his work with a series of research grants.

With this support, the thirty-three-year-old professor manned his laboratory with the college's brightest graduate students and launched a spectacular series of studies into every phase of steroid chemistry. Within barely 8 years he published a startling total of 147 scientific papers and devised new processing methods upon which he secured over 70 patents which were assigned to Parke, Davis & Co.

It was during this period that Marker became convinced that plentiful plant materials could be found from which sex steroids might be far more efficiently and cheaply produced than from animal raw materials. He knew, for example, that many plants of the lily family—including the sarsaparilla, yucca, agave, and true yam—contained in their roots substantial quantities of compounds called sapogenins. Every molecule of these sapogenins included the basic four-ring nucleus of carbon atoms, typical of all steroids. And all of them had a long side chain extending from the 17 position of their fourth carbon ring. In this respect they very much resembled cholesterol, the "starting material" from which our bodies synthesize the natural sex hormones. In our minuscule human hormone factories —the testes, ovaries, and adrenal cortex—the long cholesterol side chain is easily chopped off by nature's efficient chemical processes. But to perform this chopping operation on sapogenins required a chemical wizardry no one had dared attempt.

Marker, however, refused to be influenced by the timidity of other chemists. At State College he managed first to determine the exact configuration of the sapogenin side chain and then, in just a few months during 1940, developed an efficient, five-stage process of degrading the side chain and converting sapogenins into progesterone. With just three more processing stages he turned progesterone into testosterone.

That year and the next Russell Marker spent his summer vacation in the Southwest and in Mexico, collecting the roots of scores of different sapogenin-secreting plants. He also enlisted the aid of seventeen American and Mexican botanists who made similar collections for him. Soon the laboratories at State College were crammed to overflowing with more than a hundred thousand pounds of over four hundred different species of plants. And Marker and his students kept the lab lights burning all night for months on end as they analyzed each plant to determine its sapogenin content.

About half of the specimens yielded nothing. But others contained anywhere from a trace to substantial percentages of twelve different and previously unknown types of sapogenin. Marker named one pennogenin for Pennsylvania State College, another was designated rockogenin after Dean Frank C. "Rocky" Whitmore, and a third, kammogenin in honor of Oliver Kamm, research director of Parke, Davis. But the richest of all the sapogenins, Marker determined, was the substance called diosgenin, derived from the roots of the *Dioscorea* plant, the wild yam which grows in the even wilder mountains of southern Mexico.

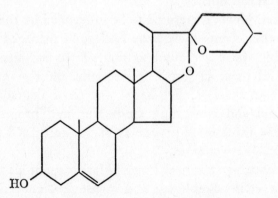

Diosgenin, extracted from *Dioscorea* roots, the starting material from which chemists create synthetic steroid hormones.

With diosgenin, and his methods of converting it into sex steroids, Marker was certain that he could break the European grip on hormone production and provide the world with an unlimited source of low-cost mass-produced hormones that would permit doctors to relieve the suffering of millions.

All sorts of reasons, however, were adduced against Marker's project. The *Dioscorea* roots would have to be brought out of the roughest of rough country with no roads save Indian trails and with no potential labor force save untrained and disinterested Indians. Mexican politics were unstable. Mexico had neither scientists nor technicians capable of running a hormone processing plant. Hundreds of thousands of dollars of capital would have to be risked just getting set for production.

And who knew whether, by then, European or American chemists would not have found equally effective ways of improving the old methods of hormone extraction? Yields, from ox bile and animal glands and cows' spinal cords and sheep's wool grease, were all improving. Soybeans also looked like a promising new starting material and they could be grown by the millions of bushels right in the Midwest.

For two years Marker argued and pleaded in vain. Then, in the middle of a school term, he broke his connections with Parke, Davis and walked out of State College just as abruptly as he had left the University of Maryland and the Rockefeller Institute. In Mexico City he rented a back-street cottage with a backyard shed where pottery had once been made. Then he set out for the hill country west of Veracruz and bought a mule, a spade, a machete, and a couple of dozen burlap coffee bags.

He knew none of the Indian languages and only a smattering of Spanish. But he managed to convey to the natives that he was looking for the vine they called *cabeza de negro,* this being the *Dioscorea mexicana,* whose roots contained up to 5 percent or more of diosgenin.

The natives looked at him and laughed at the very thought that anyone would come from far off to collect the roots of the *cabeza de negro.* But they showed him how to recognize the plant by its heart-shaped leaves and tiny flowers, and even helped him with his digging. Thus, within a few weeks, Marker returned to Mexico City with enough bagfuls of root to get to work in the makeshift lab he had set up in the old pottery shed.

Here Marker started extracting diosgenin from his roots, chopping off the long side chain in improvised kettles and retorts, and shifting atoms from one position to another in the steroid molecule. He employed no help, for he could afford none. He observed no regular working hours. But in just two months of lonely, feverish activity, during the summer of 1943, he produced nearly four and a half pounds of progesterone, worth $160,000 at the then current price of $80 a gram.

Now the former professor walked into the office of Laboratorios Hermona. This small firm had been founded in 1932 by two émigrés from Hungary: a lawyer, Dr. Emeric Somlo, and a physician, Dr. Frederick Lehmann. They produced some hormone extracts and imported others. On Lehmann's desk Marker set down two newspaper-wrapped bundles. Then he casually unwrapped one of them to reveal a kilogram jar. And quite as casually he explained that the slightly more than two pounds of white powder that filled it was progesterone which he had made himself—more progesterone than anyone else in the world had ever seen in a single batch.

It took Lehmann ten minutes to get over his utter astonishment. Then he reached for the phone and called Somlo who was in New York on business. In a flood of fluent Hungarian they agreed that they had a maverick on their hands, but one much too brilliant to let go. If this really were progesterone, and they soon made sure it was, they wanted not only to buy it but to sew up the services and the know-how of the quiet little man who had made it.

A few days of stubborn bargaining followed before Marker realized that he had broken the world price for progesterone merely by revealing what a vast quantity he could produce. At last he agreed to sell his two kilograms for substantially less than $160,000. And a few weeks after that Marker, Somlo, and Lehmann incorporated a new firm, Syntex Sociedad Anónima, with Marker holding 40 percent of the stock and Somlo and Lehmann sharing the rest.

Over the next year Marker turned out ten more kilograms of progesterone which his two partners sold as quietly as they could to pharmaceutical houses all over the world. But although they extracted pledges of secrecy from their customers, word was soon out that Syntex had cracked the European hormone monopoly. Buyers insisted on lower prices which Syntex—making a fantastic profit, thanks to Marker's high-yield process—gradually granted. By 1945 the retail price of the sex hormones had fallen by almost half and physicians everywhere were prescribing them in quantities many times greater than ever before.

A year later a dispute arose between Marker and his associates in Syntex. Selling them his interest in the firm, he formed a new steroid producing company, Hormosynth S. A. For a time he continued his active research work and published a number of additional papers. Then in 1952 he left Hormosynth and became even more of a recluse.

Recently Dr. Gregory Pincus of the Worcester Foundation for Experimental Biology, who used to correspond regularly with Professor Marker, said he had been trying to find the gifted chemist for a number of years, but with no success. Mail sent to his old headquarters at the Hotel Geneve in Mexico City comes back marked "no forwarding address." A number of major pharmaceutical houses have also spent extensive sums in fruitless searches for Marker, whose services they would gladly engage were he available. Periodically a rumor spreads that Marker has been seen in one tiny Mexican village or another. His old friends in Mexico and in the States have repeatedly checked out such rumors but always have failed to find him. Today no one seems to know for certain whether or not he is alive.

But though Marker has disappeared, the industry he founded has continued to flourish. It provides employment for thousands of root gatherers, and it has fostered the development of a small army of highly skilled Mexican chemists and technicians where there were virtually none a generation ago. Its exports of finished steroids and partly processed steroid precursors bring to Mexico more than $60,000,000 a year in urgently needed foreign exchange.

"It is difficult to understand," writes the consulting biochemist Norman Applezweig, "why the Mexican government has not yet seen fit to officially honor Russell Marker. He worked without the aid of modern instruments, using only the 'geographer's' intuition of the classical organic chemist to chart the intricate structures of the steroid sapogenins. As though this were not enough, he then turned with the same intensity to the commercial extraction of these compounds and their conversion to sex hormones. Single-handedly he created an industry which has brought vast wealth and prestige to Mexico and immeasurable benefits to the health of many millions throughout the world."

While Marker was a partner in Syntex, he performed all the key chemical operations himself in a jury-rigged laboratory shed behind the Syntex offices, and he kept no records of his procedures. And so, when he parted from his partners, Drs. Somlo and Lehmann were left high and dry with a process they did not know how to carry out. Fortunately for them, they were able to hire George Rosenkranz, a former student of the Nobel Prize-winning steroid chemist Leopold Ruzicka. Almost overnight Rosenkranz managed to "re-invent" Marker's diosgenin extracting and processing procedures. Within less than two months Syntex was again producing progesterone.

For a number of years, Syntex enjoyed a virtual monopoly of the production of steroids from plant materials, largely because the Mexican government had embargoed the export not only of *Dioscorea* root but also of the hormone precursors prepared by processing diosgenin. But in 1955, Dr. Irving V. Sollins—who had been director of Syntex's United States subsidiary for sales and research—formed a new firm, Productos Esteroides S. A., with a modern *Dioscorea* processing plant in Mexico City and its own root-gathering and drying facilities in the hill country. The competition of Pesa, as it inevitably came to be called, brought about further substantial reductions in sex steroid prices.

In 1961 an American firm, G. D. Searle & Co., absorbed Sollins' interests and has greatly enlarged both the root-gathering and manufacturing operations. Meanwhile, as the demand for steroids soared, other plants were established in Mexico. Today, in addition to the Searle and Syntex plants, extensive processing facilities are operated by subsidiaries of three other American firms—Smith, Kline & French Laboratories, the Schering Corp., and the Wyeth Laboratories Division of the American Home Products Corp.—as well as by the German Schering pharmaceutical interests.

In recent years the *cabeza de negro* has been almost completely replaced by another sub-species of *Dioscorea*, barbasco, whose roots have a higher diosgenin content. But the root-gathering operation is still essentially the same as it was when Professor Marker first organized his collecting stations. The actual digging out of the root is performed almost entirely by Mexican Indians during the "off season"—that is, after the bean, banana, coffee, orange, and sugar cane crops have been harvested. At such times groups of these workers follow the mountain trails into jungle country where the barbasco vines cling for support to the larger trees. Here, with shovel and mattock, they dig out the coal-black roots which vary in weight from a pound or two to as much as forty. Chopping these into lumps, they fill as many bags as they can carry and tote them on their backs to collecting stations where the roots are weighed and paid for.

At most of these stations the roots are first separated from stones and other debris and then run through a small mill which chops them into inch-sized chunks. These chunks are spread out on concrete platforms or patios that are often as large as a football field. Here, under the hot tropical sun, the roots dry out from an original water content of 80 percent to one of as little as 3 percent. With their weight thus reduced by nearly four fifths, the dried roots are rebagged and shipped by truck to the Mexico City processing plants.

While most collecting stations still use these primitive drying methods, the Searle subsidiary Pesa has developed a much more efficient process at its central station in Plapacyaon in the mountainous southwestern corner of the State of Veracruz. Here trucks drive up a two-hundred-foot hill to dump their loads onto a concrete storage platform. Portable conveyors lift the raw root and feed it, first into a grinding mill and then into the upper end of a large concrete chute. In this the roots descend, by gravity, to a washing machine located partway down the hill. With dirt and pebbles removed the roots again slide down the chute to further holding stages, since it has been found that the extraction of diosgenin is facilitated if they remain for a day or two in this "super-wetted" condition. Then the root chunks descend once more into a huge rotary drying kiln from which they emerge as a powder with their water content reduced to barely one percent.

In order to prevent the depletion of the barbasco supply, the Mexican government has instituted an elaborate conservation and surveying program. Each company is permitted to purchase and process an annual quota of raw root. A tax is levied against every ton of root and these funds support a corps of forestry experts who periodically survey the mountainous countryside to decide whether partially depleted areas should be closed to root gathering until nature has replenished the supply of mature plants. Currently the steroid processing companies are allowed annual quotas totaling about forty-three thousand tons of raw root, an amount calculated by the Mexican Conservation Service as just balanced with the annual new growth of barbasco root. The rapid expansion of other forms of agriculture in Mexico, however, is gradually reducing the forest acreage. Thus no one can be certain that the root supply, which is currently sufficient to meet international needs for finished steroids, will remain so indefinitely.

The very rapidly expanding demand for steroid drugs further complicates this situation. Almost all the principal

steroid producing companies, therefore, are actively searching for new plant sources of raw material. One possibility,
of course, lies in non-Mexican sources of *Dioscorea*, since
varieties of this plant are native to portions of Central and
South America, India, Japan, China, and Africa. A number
of European pharmaceutical houses have recently bought
quantities of *Dioscorea* root from Communist China.

Since such purchases by American firms are prohibited, a
number of them have been carrying on extensive experiments in the cultivation of the barbasco vine as a field crop.
One such major effort was initiated some years ago by Dr.
Sollins and his associates in Puerto Rico and has been continued in Mexico by the Searle Company. Because the diosgenin content of barbasco roots varies greatly—from a
fraction of a percent to an occasional 7 or 8 percent—it was
originally thought that selected, diosgenin-rich plants could
be propagated for annual harvest. It was later found, however, that diosgenin accumulates in the plant roots over a
period of years and that cultivated plants would have to be
allowed to remain in the soil for three, four, or five years
before their roots yielded sufficient diosgenin to justify their
harvesting.

Under these circumstances, to use crop land solely to
raise *Dioscorea* would be uneconomical. Current experiments thus are built around the idea of inter-cropping—that
is, corn or similar plants are grown in alternate rows with
the *Dioscorea*, thereby providing an annual harvest while
the maturation of the *Dioscorea* roots is awaited. This plan
offers another advantage as well, since the *Dioscorea* vine
which normally grows up the trunk of a tree needs some
similar support to flourish under cultivation. On experimental acreage the vines have done well when able to find
the support of adjacent corn stalks.

Another promising source of steroid raw material is the plant species *Solanum aviculari* from which a sterol called solasodine can be isolated. While its side chain structure differs somewhat from that of diosgenin, processes have been developed for chopping it off and then rebuilding the steroid nucleus into active hormones. In this country and in Mexico, Searle horticultural experts have had marked success in preliminary experiments in the cultivation of *Solanum* as an annual plant with a high per-acre yield.

If such field cultivation proves practicable, it would be possible to grow *Solanum* under a wide variety of climatic conditions within no more than a one- to two-hundred-mile radius from the processing plants in Mexico City. By varying planting schedules the harvesting of the *Solanum* crop could be timed to assure a continuous supply during the months in which harvesting of other crops prevents the digging of barbasco root.

Still another possibility lies in the extraction of sterols from varieties of the agave plant which grows wild in the Southwest of the United States, in northern Mexico, in East Africa, and in Central America. Much research is also going on in both the United States and Europe in the extraction of the sterol tomatidine from the leaves of certain wild varieties of tomato plants.

Whether or not one or more of these efforts toward the cultivation of sterol-yielding crops proves economical, another factor is at work to ward off a steroid shortage. For pharmaceutical chemists gradually have been increasing the yield of steroid end-products they are able to derive from a given quantity of starting sterol. At the G. D. Searle plant at Skokie, Illinois, for example, one stage in the processing of certain steroid compounds formerly had a yield of slightly under 20 percent; five grams of precursor material were necessary to produce a single gram for the next higher stage of processing. Within the last year, however, a modification of this chemical step has raised its yield to over 40 percent. In effect, the improvement of this one single stage of a long multi-stage process has doubled the quantity of end-product steroid that can be obtained from every pound of starting material.

Should all of these alternative methods of increasing or extending the supply of plant materials for steroid production still fall short of meeting the ever-growing demand for steroid compounds, manufacturers have yet another recourse. American and European chemists have developed a number of methods of total synthesis by which a wide variety of steroids can be created out of such common starting materials as petroleum derivatives and alcohols. Today such methods cannot compete with processes relying upon vegetable steroids. But they stand, in reserve as it were, as an ever-ready guarantee against a world-wide steroid shortage that would deprive physicians and their patients of compounds upon which many millions have come to rely.

4

•

THE CORTISONE

FAMINE

•

For more than seventy years after Dr. Joseph Addison identified the wasting-away of the adrenal glands as the cause of
the disease that bears his name, physicians had no effective
method of treating it. Their diagnoses of cases meant little
more than the reading of a death sentence, for the life expectancy of victims of Addison's disease was barely six
months.

Then in 1924 at The Johns Hopkins Hospital in Baltimore, two young doctors, Samuel J. Crowe and George Bernays Wislocki, performed a crucial series of experiments. First, they removed the inner cores or medullae of the adrenal glands from a number of laboratory dogs. The animals survived and even frisked about in their cages. Next, they operated on a second group of dogs, removing only the cortices of their adrenal glands and leaving the medullae intact. This time, each operation resulted in the rapid development of the typical symptoms of Addison's disease, followed by the dogs' early death. The Baltimore researchers had pinpointed the cause of Addison's malady: a deficiency of adrenal *cortex* hormone.

Other experimenters were quick to take the next logical step. In 1927, at Western Reserve University in Cleveland, Drs. Julius M. Rogoff and George N. Stewart prepared an extract of the adrenal cortices of dogs and used it to prolong the lives of other dogs whose own adrenals had been removed. In that same year two brothers, Drs. Frank A. and W. E. Hartman, and Dr. Katherine A. Brownell saved the lives of adrenalectomized dogs with a cortical extract. And in 1930 Professor Wilbur W. Swingle of Princeton University teamed up with twenty-six-year-old biochemist Joseph Pfiffner to prepare still another extract—from the adrenal cortices of cattle—which was placed on the market by Parke, Davis & Co. Other pharmaceutical houses quickly brought forth similar extracts.

Using these new preparations, physicians were able to extend the lives of sufferers from Addison's disease. Unfortunately, many of these early extracts varied greatly in potency from one lot to another. Some were contaminated with adrenaline, the hormone of the adrenal medulla, which often caused severe reactions. But by this time researchers in numerous pharmaceutical laboratories were hard at work in the hunt for methods of preparing purer and more potent cortical extracts. By 1935 Dr. Marvin H. Kuizenga of the Upjohn Co. succeeded in making an adrenaline-free cortex extract of standardized potency—and the outlook for sufferers from Addison's disease changed completely. Today almost all such patients can look forward to the total relief of their symptoms and a nearly normal life expectancy.

In the mid-1930s no one knew whether these new cortical extracts contained one hormone or many. But the very nature of Addison's disease, evoking as it did so many varied symptoms, lent great weight to the supposition that the adrenal cortex produced more than one, and probably many different hormones. Thus steroid chemists, fresh from their triumphant isolations of testosterone, estrogen, and progesterone, could not resist the challenge presented by the adrenal extracts. From 1935 onward four teams of such researchers engaged in a frantic though friendly race to isolate and identify the substance—or substances—that made these extracts so effective a weapon against adrenal hypofunction.

Moving from Princeton in 1935, Dr. Pfiffner joined forces with Drs. Oscar Wintersteiner and Harry M. Vars of the Columbia University Department of Biochemistry. By the end of 1936 they were able to report the isolation from adrenal extracts of four different hormones, all of them steroids. And there remained an "amorphous" fraction, whose potency indicated that additional hormones were contained within it.

At the Mayo Foundation, biochemist Edward C. Kendall —who back in 1914 had discovered the thyroid hormone, thyroxine—also attacked the adrenal extracts. Within little more than a year he, together with Drs. Harold L. Mason and Charles S. Myers, had isolated five pure crystalline compounds, three of which later were found to be identical with three of those discovered by the Columbia group.

In Switzerland, meanwhile, Dr. Tadeus Reichstein had made extracts from the adrenal glands of more than twenty thousand cattle from which he had derived less than an ounce of highly active hormone substance. Breaking this down, he eventually identified more than twenty-five steroid compounds, including six biologically active hormones.

Finally, at the Upjohn laboratories, Drs. Kuizenga and George F. Cartland carried on a similar project, using extracts of hog adrenals in place of the cattle adrenal extracts of the three other teams.

Thus, by 1940, more than thirty pure crystalline substances had been isolated from the complex mixture of compounds that could be extracted from the adrenal glands. (Since then, this number of known adrenal secretions, active and inactive, has risen to forty-six.) But, all of these remained, for a time at least, mere academic curiosities. No one had thought of any practical use for them except in the treatment of Addison's disease. And there seemed to be little point in going through the tremendously expensive process of refining these new steroids since adrenal insufficiency already could be effectively treated with a simple "porridge" extract.

Then, in the fall of 1941, military intelligence agents picked up a rumor that the Germans were buying vast quantities of adrenal glands in Argentina. About the same time, an American researcher, exploring the effect of cortical extracts upon laboratory rats, observed that they seemed to increase the resistance of these animals to the stress of oxygen deprivation. This was enough to balloon the first rumor into one even more alarming: that Nazi pilots were able to fly to forty thousand feet and higher because they were being hopped up with injections of an adrenal cortex hormone.

Eager to get its hands on this wonder drug, the Air Force turned to the National Research Defense Council, which set into motion a crash program of adrenal cortex research involving every laboratory in the United States and Canada where any work had been done on adrenal extracts.

But even the research teams at the Mayo Foundation, Columbia, and the Upjohn labs had been able to isolate barely enough pure cortical substances from extracts to determine their steroid structures. It quickly became apparent that any attempt to produce an altitude-tolerance-booster steroid for the thousands of fighter pilots we were training would require so many millions of adrenals that all the cattle and hogs in the entire country would have to be slaughtered. Thus Merck & Co., a chemical and pharmaceutical house already strong in synthetic chemistry, was asked to undertake a special crash program of its own: an attempt to synthesize duplicates of cortical hormones from more abundant starting materials.

Merck's Dr. Lewis H. Sarett first set out to make Kendall's Compound A, now known as 11-dehydrocorticosterone. It differed from all previously known steroids in that it had an oxygen atom attached to the number-11 position of its steroid nucleus. No one, up to then, had ever faced the formidable problem of artificially tacking an oxygen atom onto this position on a steroid. But Dr. Sarett chose as his starting material beef bile, both because it was available in large quantities as a packing-house waste product and because he could easily derive from it a steroid called desoxycholic acid, which has an oxygen and a hydrogen atom attached to the adjacent position, number 12, on its steroid nucleus. His hope: to find a way of moving that single oxygen atom from position 12 to position 11.

After spending endless hours and scores of thousands of dollars, Sarett and his assistants succeeded in accomplishing this bit of chemical magic by a process involving more than thirty separate chemical reactions. They prepared several hundred grams of Compound A. But it proved to have no useful biological activity in man.

By this time new intelligence reports had made it clear that the Germans had not been buying unusual quantities of adrenal cortices in Argentina and had, in fact, never developed any kind of chemical altitude-tolerance booster. But Sarett's research had gained momentum, and the Merck officials allowed him to add a few more steps to his complex process to make Kendall's Compound E. Only five grams were synthesized because there seemed to be no point in making any more. World War II, in fact, had already ended when four grams of Compound E were sent to various medical researchers who found it quite effective against Addison's disease. But Upjohn chemists, by then, had extracted from adrenal tissues another steroid, Compound F, which proved even more potent than Sarett's preparation in relieving the disease. Thus, his last gram of Compound E was put on a storeroom shelf.

It might have remained there indefinitely—or even eventually been thrown out—had Dr. Philip S. Hench, the Mayo Clinic's outstanding rheumatologist, not been a friend of chemist Kendall. Over many years Dr. Hench had observed that women suffering from rheumatoid arthritis frequently experienced remissions shortly after becoming pregnant—remissions which lasted until they had delivered their babies. He had noted, too, that arthritics who developed infectious jaundice experienced similar remissions, some of which lasted for many months. He interpreted both phenomena as instances of the sort of stress known to stimulate the adrenal cortex into producing large quantities of hormones. And he had, therefore, actually tried cortical extracts on some of his patients. But here he had failed, because the best of these extracts were simply not potent enough.

Early in July of 1948 a young woman was referred to Dr. Hench at the Mayo Clinic. She was only twenty-nine, but she had already suffered through almost five years of unceasing pain. She had gone through all the then available treatments for arthritis one by one—the massive doses of vitamin E, the injections of gold salts, the hot baths, the sun-bakings. But none of these had helped her.

When Dr. Hench first examined her, she looked like a woman of fifty—a desperately sick woman of fifty. Her joints were stiff, swollen, excruciatingly tender. Her right hip was so far gone that she walked, when she walked at all, with a weird shuffling gait. And after three months, during which Dr. Hench had tried every treatment he knew, her joints were more swollen, more painful than ever.

In utter frustration Hench turned to Kendall and asked whether he still had any of that Compound E in his lab. Kendall answered, "No." But seeing the dismal look on Hench's face, he added, "Wait a minute. Maybe Sarett has some of it." Then he put in a long-distance call to Merck in Rahway, New Jersey, and set Dr. Sarett hunting through his storeroom shelves.

The next morning—September 21, 1948—an air-mail, special-delivery package reached Dr. Hench. He opened it, read the label, and went to the desperate young woman's room. There, he filled a syringe and injected her with Compound E—now known as cortisone.

That day and the next—when she received a second injection—Compound E seemed to her to be no better than all of the other preparations with which she has been dosed.

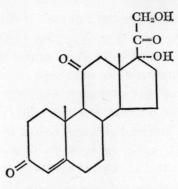

Dr. Kendall's Compound E

Her pains continued unabated. On the third day, she woke in the faint light of dawn and—as she had done thousands of times before—she postponed her day's ordeal by keeping perfectly still for a moment; a moment marred only by the certainty that as soon as she moved, pain would grip her again.

Then she rolled over onto her side—and stopped.

Something was wrong—but marvelously wrong.

She had tensed herself for a piercing surge of pain. But it hadn't occurred. She moved her arms. Still no pain. Slowly, she lifted her legs and set them down on the floor. When Dr. Hench arrived he was astonished to find her standing without support in the middle of the room. Gay and smiling, she showed him how easily she could move, how the swellings in her joints had diminished.

The next morning when she woke, her stiffness was entirely gone. Scarcely able to rise from her bed three days before, she now paced across the room like a perfectly healthy woman, her unclenched hands outstretched to greet her wonder-working physician.

Four days later, after only seven doses of the strange new drug, she dressed herself and left the hospital. For the first time in years she set out on a shopping tour, strolling for more than three hours through Rochester's busy, downtown stores. She returned tired, but neither stiff nor sore. And in all Minnesota that day, it would have been hard to find a happier woman.

But Dr. Hench was not nearly as happy. To treat this one patient he had used up nearly a quarter of his now infinitely precious gram of cortisone. Unless he could treat other patients and get similar results, he would have no way of knowing whether this one woman's remission was due to cortisone or whether it was merely some lucky coincidence.

Again he turned to his friend Ed Kendall. And this time both of them got on the phone to Lew Sarett. "No," Sarett told them, "there isn't another speck of cortisone in existence." Then he added, "But hold on. We'll try to make you some."

Sarett knew that he was committing his company to expenditures of incalculable amounts. But he also knew that with just the possibility that cortisone might really turn out to be an effective weapon against arthritis, no one at Merck would complain. Calling his assistants off other work, he began re-rigging his Rube Goldberg arrangement of flasks and tubes and retorts, and rerunning his thirty-six-step cortisone-synthesizing process. In a few days he was able to mail one gram of cortisone to the Mayo Clinic. Within a few weeks he had produced nearly a kilogram of cortisone, enough to enable Hench and Kendall to treat thirteen additional patients for almost six months.

Dr. Hench deliberately selected these patients from among the most painfully crippled in the Clinic. Some had been able to get about only in wheelchairs. Yet after just a few days of injections with cortisone the knots in their muscles had untied; the swellings in their joints had subsided, then vanished; they had put on weight; they had walked; some had even danced.

But Phil Hench was an old hand at arthritis. He had seen too many such "miracles" before. He knew that now and then—under any form of treatment, and sometimes under no treatment at all—a crippling case of arthritis reversed its course and vanished as inexplicably as it had come. He also knew that all too often such remissions quickly faded and left the arthritic as crippled as before.

Thus he waited, week after week, for these *cortisone* remissions to end. But the relapses he feared simply did not occur. As long as he continued his daily injections of cortisone all fourteen of his patients remained virtually free of all symptoms of arthritis.

At the end of six months Dr. Hench knew that the time had come to tell his medical colleagues of his discovery. At a physicians' meeting in April, 1949, the lights were turned down and a color film began flickering on the screen. First came the "before treatment" pictures, in which patients with characteristically deformed joints struggled to totter a few steps. Suddenly an electrifying gasp swept through his audience as the first of the "after treatment" scenes appeared and the doctors saw the very same patients jauntily climbing steps, swinging their arms and legs, and even doing little jigs as if they had never been crippled at all.

Even before the film ended, the watching physicians had filled the hall with wave after wave of resounding applause. When the lights went up and Dr. Hench approached the lectern, he was greeted with a standing ovation. But when he was able to speak at last, he tried to quench their enthusiasm with a series of distressing facts.

The patients they had just seen had all been treated with cortisone synthesized by Dr. Sarett of Merck. This synthetic duplicate of an adrenal hormone, however, was not a *cure* for rheumatoid arthritis. It simply alleviated the symptoms of the disease—*as long as it was regularly administered.*

Moreover, the new hormone had not been made in a factory, but rather had been prepared in tiny quantities in the laboratory by a fantastically complicated and fantastically expensive process. Every dose Dr. Hench had administered had cost Merck more than $1,000 to produce.

Worse still, many months would have to pass before Merck's chemists could produce enough cortisone to permit even experimental use by other arthritis specialists in other hospitals. And no one knew how much additional time would elapse before factory production of cortisone could get under way, nor how costly the factory's product would prove to be when it finally became widely available.

The next morning, under front-page headlines, newspapers throughout the world carried the astounding story of the patients who danced. In most papers, however, Dr. Hench's solemn words of warning appeared, if at all, only many paragraphs down and in small type. Thus, millions of arthritics rushed to their family physicians in the innocent belief that they could start upon a course of cortisone injections immediately. But their hopes which had been suddenly raised so high were just as suddenly dashed. The prompt relief from pain and crippling that they had been led to expect had to be denied them in the face of a cortisone famine.

How long that famine would last no one could predict. Every major pharmaceutical concern in the country was anxious to play a role in ending the tragic shortage of cortisone. But as these firms assessed the tremendous technical difficulties with which they would be faced, one after another reluctantly decided that it could not hope to overtake Merck's lead. In the end, only two—Upjohn and G. D. Searle & Co.—joined Merck in the race to make cortisone quickly available in great quantities and inexpensively enough so that all who needed it could have it.

Upjohn, long a leading producer of adrenal extracts, already had a large staff of outstanding steriod researchers at its command. Now, under a new research director, Dr. Richard S. Schreiber, it started not just one cortisone-seeking project but a half dozen. By midsummer of 1949, more than 150 Upjohn scientists and technicians were busily engaged in the largest research effort any pharmaceutical company had ever launched.

One team of chemists set to work in an attempt to simplify Merck's bile-acid method of producing cortisone. A second group tried to synthesize cortisone directly from cheap coal-tar chemicals. A third set of chemists worked with inexpensive ergosterol as a starting material. In adjacent laboratories another group sought to convert into cortisone an extract of the common hellebore plant. Still another team, botanists this time, were sent to Africa to search for a rare subspecies of the *Strophanthus* family of vines, the seeds of which had been reported to contain a sapogenin with an oxygen atom already in the 11 position.

Like Merck and Upjohn, Searle was one of America's oldest pharmaceutical houses, though far smaller in 1949 than either of its competitors in the cortisone race. It had been founded in 1888 by a Hoosier pharmacist, Gideon Daniel Searle. In those days rural doctors seldom wrote prescriptions, since their patients had no easy access to drug stores. Instead, physicians customarily purchased their favorite medicaments from so-called "pill houses" and dispensed them from their little black bags. Thousands of such dispensing physicians had come to depend upon Gideon Searle's company because of the reliability of its products and its willingness to prepare and stock a broad range of preparations. At one point, in fact, Gideon's catalog listed more than a thousand products, including over 400 fluid extracts, 115 elixirs, 100 syrups, 30 medicinal wines, and over 150 botanical drugs.

Gideon Searle's son Claude Howard had been more interested in medicine than in manufacturing. He had graduated from Rush Medical College in 1898, but defying the custom of the time, he had not gone immediately into private practice. Instead, he did a year of postgraduate work at the University of Chicago and then "interned"— before that term had been invented—for two years more at St. Joseph's Hospital under the distinguished surgeons Drs. Nicholas Senn and John B. Murphy. Then he had moved with his bride to the little Mississippi River town of Sabula, Iowa. There his unusually complete training quickly won him so large a practice that he had to maintain three teams of horses and a man to drive his buggy so that he could get his sleep in cat naps between calls.

But in 1909, when aging Gideon Searle suffered a stroke, the young doctor reluctantly gave up his practice, moved his family to Chicago, and took over the management of his father's firm. One of his first moves was to set up a research department, long before most other drug manufacturers did so. Thus his company developed such specialties as the first American-made arsenical drug for the treatment of syphilis.

Dr. Searle had begun to train his son Jack in the intricacies of his business even before the youngster reached his teens. As soon as Jack Searle won his degree in pharmacy at the University of Michigan, in 1923, he was brought into the firm with the title of Treasurer and a salary of $35 a week.

By then the country, and with it the practice of medicine, was rapidly changing. Drug stores, operated by well-trained pharmacists, had been opened even in small towns, and the number of dispensing physicians was on the decline. So John Searle began consistently to cut down the company's vast line of elixirs and tinctures and simultaneously to build up its research efforts. By 1936, when he succeeded his father in the presidency of the firm, G. D. Searle & Co. was producing only twenty pharmaceutical items; and Jack Searle was determined that it would add to this line only original contributions to the improvement of medical practice developed in its own laboratories.

To help carry out this decision Jack Searle induced Dr. Albert L. Raymond, a specialist in carbohydrate metabolism, to leave his position as an Associate at the Rockefeller Institute and join Searle as its Director of Research. At the same time, as a matter of long-range policy, the company began to spend a higher proportion of its income on research than any other in the pharmaceutical field. At its new laboratories, erected in 1941 in the Chicago suburb of Skokie, it provided Dr. Raymond and his growing staff of brilliant young chemists, biologists, and clinicians with every modern research facility. There they developed Dramamine, the first drug designed to prevent motion sickness, and Banthine, one of medicine's most effective weapons in the treatment of peptic ulcers. By 1949 these and a half dozen other original contributions to the physician's armament accounted for over two thirds of Searle's output.

For half a dozen years Searle grants had helped support the extensive steroid research activities of the Worcester Foundation for Experimental Biology. Dr. Gregory Pincus, a co-director of the Foundation, also served Searle as a consultant. And at the Searle laboratories, Dr. Raymond had begun to develop a specialized Steroid Research Group under the direction of Dr. Byron Riegel, Northwestern University's distinguished Professor of Biochemistry.

Thus, though still a tiny David compared with the two Goliaths, Merck and Upjohn, Searle had thoroughly qualified itself to join the scientific contest it now entered.

At the Worcester Foundation, beginning in 1945, Dr. Pincus and Dr. Oscar Hechter had been developing an original and ingenious method of exploring the complex chains of chemical reactions by which human or animal glands synthesized hormones. From an experimental animal they would remove an entire gland—a testicle, an ovary, an adrenal, or a liver—and mount it intact in a specially designed glass apparatus. Then they would pump a continuous stream of blood or serum through the fresh gland to keep it alive and functioning as a natural steroid "factory." By analyzing the chemical composition of the blood at the start of a perfusion period and re-analyzing it periodically, they were able to determine each step by which the gland broke down a starting material, such as cholesterol, and then built it up into hormones.

By 1949 a whole series of technical bugs had been eliminated from the Worcester perfusion method. Thus, with the outbreak of the cortisone famine, Drs. Pincus and Hechter and their team of biochemists and physiologists were ready to carry through a crucial new experiment. They placed a fresh beef adrenal gland into a glass perfusion cell. They prepared a solution similar to blood serum and added to it an inexpensive steroid material which lacked an oxygen atom in the key number-11 position. Then they flipped a switch, started their pump going, and ran the liquid through the preserved gland. When they stopped their apparatus and analyzed the perfused solution they found that the enzymes within the gland had accomplished almost the entire series of chemical transformations that Lewis Sarett had so laboriously achieved in his cortisone-synthesizing process. In a single operation they were able to go directly from a starting material to hydrocortisone.

Now at the Searle plant in Skokie engineers worked round the clock, tearing out laboratory walls and erecting batteries of perfusion devices. They developed special pumps to circulate perfusion solutions through glass manifolds, which distributed them to row upon row of cells, each containing a fresh beef adrenal. Periodically technicians worked their way down each row, removing exhausted glands from the cells and replacing them with fresh ones. Every few hours the perfused solutions were taken away in large glass carboys to an adjacent section where the precious cortisone was extracted from them.

Jack Searle and Al Raymond were well aware that their array of hundreds of perfusion cells, each containing a single adrenal gland, did not represent an economically practical method of producing cortisone. They hoped eventually to re-engineer the process and thus lower production costs. But meanwhile they deliberately ignored commercial considerations in order to provide cortisone quickly to clinicians and their suffering patients. By mid-1950 Searle was supplying substantial quantities of this steroid, without charge, to scores of clinical researchers all over the United States.

Merck's chemists and engineers, of course, had not been idle during these long months. Under the direction of Dr. Max Tishler they had scaled up Lewis Sarett's process, first to pilot-plant size and then to a multimillion-dollar factory. At step after step in the long process they had managed to improve yields. Late in 1949 they were able to offer cortisone acetate to physicians, in limited amounts and at $200 a gram. By late 1950 they had produced their first thousand kilograms and the price was reduced to $35 a gram.

Meanwhile, in Kalamazoo, most of Upjohn's cortisone-seeking projects had bogged down. But the Hechter-Pincus demonstration that cortisone could be made by a natural method of *biosynthesis*—and the Searle Company's proof that this method could be stepped up toward something resembling mass production—inspired one Upjohn research team to attempt a new biosynthetic approach of its own.

At the head of this group was Dr. Durey H. Peterson, a biochemist with long experience in antibiotic research and thus familiar with the methods by which microbes were used in fermentation processes to create such antibiotics as penicillin and streptomycin. Working with Dr. Herbert C. Murray, Dr. Samuel H. Eppstein, and other members of Upjohn's chemistry department, Dr. Peterson set out to discover whether microbes could not also be used to achieve the same chemical transformations that enzymes accomplished in the Pincus-Hechter-Searle perfusion process.

Deliberately duplicating the accident by which the mold

76/ THE HORMONE QUEST

that produced penicillin had been discovered, Dr. Murray
—the microbiologist of the team—set open, broth-filled
culture plates around his laboratory and on the window
sills. After allowing sufficient time for molds to settle upon
these plates, he turned them over to Dr. Peterson and his
other biochemist colleagues who added progesterone lacking an 11-oxygen atom to the mold-infected broth and let
it stand under moderate heat for a few hours. From the
resulting ferment they were able to recover 11-hydroxy-
progesterone. Just as they had hoped, the molds had attached an oxygen and a hydrogen atom to the number-11
position on each progesterone molecule.

Unfortunately, the randomly gathered molds had also
produced other steroids which acted as contaminants. But
the Peterson group now knew that they were on a hot
trail. The best mold they had found by the window-sill
method was a member of the *Rhizopus* group. So they sent
off to the American Type Culture Collection, a microbe
bank in Washington, for samples of numerous members
of the *Rhizopus* family. And when they tested these one
by one, a common white mold, *Rhizopus nigricans*, attacked progesterone with what can only be termed a
microbial fury.

In short order it converted almost all of the progesterone
in the broth into 11-hydroxyprogesterone. This compound
in turn lent itself readily to chemical processing into hydrocortisone, a close chemical relative of cortisone and actually more potent against arthritis than cortisone itself.
Thus, Dr. Peterson's group had discovered an extremely
inexpensive method of producing vast quantities of cortical
steroids.

During the winter of 1951–52, Upjohn's chemical engineers rushed through the designing and building of a

cortisone-producing plant. On April 7, 1952, Dr. Peterson and his colleagues published the first report on their discovery in the *Journal of the American Chemical Society*.

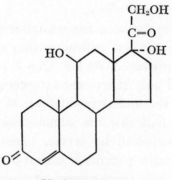

Hydrocortisone

And in May of that year, when Upjohn came into the market with hydrocortisone, the long cortical-steroid famine ended. Merck & Co., which had cut its cortisone price to $10 a gram in 1951, now reduced it still further. By 1955 cortical-steroid prices had dropped to only $3.50 a gram.

With the development of these Upjohn mass-production processes, Searle decided to withdraw from the cortisone field. It dismantled its batteries of perfusion cells and wrote off the huge sums it had invested in the race to make cortisone available to all.

But while they yielded the making of cortisone to others, Jack Searle and Al Raymond had by no means failed. Instead, as General Motors' inventive genius Charles Kettering would have put it, they had "failed forward." All through the cortisone famine their noncommercial output of this precous steroid had helped scores of clinicians carry on vitally important research studies. And at Skokie during these two years, an exceptionally able staff of chemists, biologists, and clinical researchers had been enlisted and trained, in the midst of battle as it were. In the years to come, this staff—greatly augmented—was destined to develop a long series of new synthetic steroids of tremendous medical and social usefulness.

The end of the cortisone famine, unfortunately, did not bring about the medical millenium that some enthusiasts had too freely predicted. As Dr. Hench had warned, the new drug could only relieve the symptoms of arthritis; it could not cure the underlying disease. Worse yet, physicians began to find that the administration of cortisone was often accompanied by severe, sometimes dangerous side effects. In some patients it caused a retention of salt and water that gave them a startling moon-faced appearance and put a dangerous burden on their hearts. In others it ignited peptic ulcers, caused flare-ups of tuberculosis, sent blood pressure soaring, or triggered off a form of diabetes.

But even as clinicians began to discover these drawbacks, steroid researchers were already hard at work changing and taming the cortisone molecule. By 1955 chemists at the laboratories of the Schering Corporation learned how to remove hydrogen atoms that were attached as side chains to the number-1 and number-2 positions of the cortisone nucleus. The modified hormone they created, meticortin, was more active than cortisone and could be used in smaller doses. Thus it relieved arthritis while placing less strain on the heart.

Two years later, at the Upjohn labs, chemists attached a "methyl" group of atoms to the number-6 position of the cortisone nucleus. This new synthetic, named Medrol, produced even fewer side effects in most patients than meticortin.

A bit later a research group at Lederle laboratories found a way of tacking a hydrogen-oxygen side chain onto the carbon at the number-16 position. The resulting steroid—marketed as Aristocortin by Lederle and as Kenacort by Squibb—retained cortisone's arthritis-healing power but had far less of cortisone's undesirable effect on salt-and-water balance. Almost simultaneously researchers at Merck Sharp & Dohme and Schering synthesized other modified corticoids—Decadron and Deronil—still more potent and thus usable in still smaller doses evoking still fewer, milder side effects.

Through this process of developing a battery of synthetic cortical hormones—a continuing process—physicians have been enabled to adjust their therapy to the individual needs and the individual sensitivities of their patients. Today they usually reserve all of these drugs for the fairly small number of arthritis patients who get no significant benefit from milder medications. With small doses and careful supervision even long-term treatment with cortical steroids is seldom disturbed by dangerous side effects. And at the first sign of these effects doctors can now shift from one steroid to another instead of abandoning steroid therapy entirely as they were formerly forced to do.

Nor is the usefulness of the cortical steroids limited, as it was at first, solely to rheumatoid arthritis. For clinical researchers have found that the cortical hormones are effective in relieving a whole series of diseases characterized by tissue inflammation. Thus the terror has been taken out of the kidney disease of childhood, nephrosis. Steroid therapy has revolutionized the treatment of the once-lethal inflammatory skin diseases, pemphigus and disseminated lupus erythematosus. The agonizing, life-threatening crises of what was once called intractable bronchial asthma have been brought under control with these new steroids. Eye inflammations that once led to blindness yield, often with remarkable speed, to applications of ointments containing the new corticoids. Infectious croup, which once swelled the windpipes of unlucky children and slowly choked them to death, is now frequently tamed by a steriod injection. In cases of severe burns, rheumatic fever, and numerous other infections physicians turn to cortical steroids to support their patients through a crisis and thus gain time for other treatments to take effect.

One recent tabulation, in fact, has shown that researchers have found cortical hormones useful and effective against more than 150 different disease conditions, some as common as arthritis, others, of course, much rarer. Nor is this list the final word. For despite all the advances that have been scored since Dr. Hench first tested cortisone, research goes on. Every year clinicians find a few more conditions amenable to therapy with the presently available cortical steroids. And every year steriod chemists learn how to synthesize scores of new modified cortical hormones, any one of which may yet prove to be even more useful against diseases than today's entire array of marvelously effective corticoids.

5
•

REBUILDING WASTED BODIES

•

With the end of the cortisone famine Searle's growing group of steroid experts were freed to concentrate upon other hormone research problems. Thus, at Research Board meetings, Dr. Raymond, Dr. Riegel, Dr. Francis J. Saunders, and a number of others began to hammer out a long-range policy, reviewing and analyzing various alternatives.

One obvious opportunity, of course, would be to manu-

facture duplicates of the natural androgens, estrogens, progestins, and corticosteroids, just as other companies were
doing. Under such a "me too" program, research might be
limited mainly to efforts to improve production methods and
raise yields. Commercially, such a policy would have been
quickly and highly profitable. But because it would have
been in direct conflict with the company's goal of providing
physicians with completely new products that would improve their ability to relieve or cure human ills, "me too-ism"
was unanimously ruled out.

The company decided instead to embark upon a much
more expensive and difficult course. "We called it our
separation-of-effects policy," Dr. Raymond recalls. "Our
aim was to modify the chemical structure of a natural
steroid so as to greatly enhance its desirable qualities while
breeding out its side-effect drawbacks. If, at the same time,
we could change its route of administration—so that our
modified hormone could be taken orally rather than by injection—so much the better."

Acting upon this decision, a series of research projects was
launched. The one that advanced most rapidly was an
attempt to create an anabolic steroid, one that could stimulate protein metabolism and thus hasten the rebuilding of
muscle tissues that had wasted away as a result of prolonged
illness or major surgical operations.

Earlier hormone-hunters had tracked down the male
hormone primarily with the hope of using it to transform
sexually immature males into full-fledged, fertile men. When
testosterone was finally isolated, it had indeed proved effective in promoting both the development and the potency
of the sex organs among so-called eunuchoids. But it had
done much more than that. When it was administered to

them, their squeaky soprano voices deepened; hair grew upon their previously hairless chests and chins; fat pads on their hips, abdomens, and breasts melted away and were replaced by masculine patterns of muscular growth. It was as if nature had parsimoniously decided to aim a single hormone at a multitude of targets.

Even before pure testosterone became available Drs. C. D. Kochakian and J. R. Murlin had experimentally demonstrated the anabolic, or tissue-building, properties of the male hormone. In 1935, at the University of Rochester, they had made an extract of urine gathered from their male medical students. When this was injected into castrated dogs the animals no longer poured out abnormal quantities of nitrogen in their urine. The male hormone extract had restored to them their ability to retain proteins and build them into muscle tissues. Three years later, at the University of Chicago, Dr. Allan T. Kenyon had used testosterone itself to attain the same effect on human volunteers.

But when other clinicians attempted to take advantage of testosterone's anabolic properties, they faced a major dilemma. If they administered it to women or girls, the male hormone's virilizing properties often induced growths of facial hair, voice changes, and acne, thus quickly forcing a discontinuance of treatment. Even in prepubertal boys, testosterone's desirable muscle-building effect was outbalanced by its undesirable tendency to alter bone-growth patterns. Thus the use of this natural hormone as an anabolic agent had to be restricted exclusively to mature male patients.

Between 1948 and 1955 chemists at the Searle research laboratories had synthesized more than a thousand different steroids. Now, in the Division of Biological Research, Drs.

Francis Saunders and Victor Drill and a large group of assisting technicians began the long, laborious task of screening these compounds and still others that emerged each month from the chemists' laboratories. Their object was to assay each compound for its androgenic and its anabolic activity.

To measure these activities, they used an ingenious two-way test. First they castrated a batch of thirty-day-old white laboratory rats, Twenty-one days later, when they could be sure that the rats had metabolized and excreted all of their own male hormones, they injected them, in batches, with the compound whose activity was to be measured. These intramuscular injections were repeated daily for a week. Then the rats were sacrificed and their semenal ducts, their prostate glands, and a tiny muscle called the levator ani were removed and carefully weighed.

By using an inert control material, such as corn oil, for their injections, they had established a standardized, baseline weight for each of these tissues in an average test rat. When they injected a fixed quantity of testosterone into rats, all these tissues grew and, at autopsy, the weight of each was found to have increased. Every time they repeated their testosterone injections on a new batch of rats, each tissue's weight rose by almost the same amounts as on previous tests. Since the semenal ducts and the prostate were parts of sex organs, their growth provided an accurate index of the androgenic activity of testosterone. And, because the levator ani was a muscle tissue, its weight increase measured testosterone's anabolic activity.

Thus, when they changed their injection material from testosterone to any one of the steroids they were screening, a weighing of the test rats' semenal ducts and prostates would measure the new steroid's androgenic power as compared with testosterone; while a weighing of the levator ani would provide a comparative index of the new compound's anabolic potency.

The testing of each steroid upon a batch of rats took four full weeks—from the time of castration to the final check-weighing of tissues. But by starting a number of new tests each day, Drs. Saunders and Drill were able to work their way through the screening program within less than a year. As expected, most compounds proved neither androgenic nor anabolic. A few were even more actively androgenic than testosterone. Only rarely did they find a compound that displayed even a slightly favorable ratio of anabolic to androgenic activity. But none could be by-passed in this hunt for a hypothetical needle in a chemical haystack.

Then, early in 1955, they came to a series of compounds that Searle chemist Dr. Frank Colton had put together more than a year and a half earlier. On their first test of one of these steroids the biologists got a set of figures so favorable they felt sure there must have been some slip-up in their testing technique. But when they reran their test the new figures were almost exact duplicates of the first set. The compound's anabolic index was high. But its androgenic activity was far lower than that of testosterone.

Now they put Colton's whole family of compounds to the test. And when the figures came through for a steroid with the chemical name 17-ethyl 17-hydroxynorandroste-none, they knew that they had finally found a separation of effects far beyond their most optimistic hopes. For this compound, given the generic name of norethandrolone, had all of testosterone's anabolic activity. But it exhibited on test rats only a sixteenth of the male hormone's androgenic activity.

But the new compound had to pass still other tests. Since

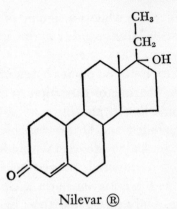

Nilevar ®

one cannot ask a rat to swallow a pill or a capsule, tiny flex-
ible tubes were slipped down the throats of new batches of
rats and solutions of steroid in corn oil were thus fed directly
into the animals' stomachs. By this method, the equivalent of
oral administration in humans, all the members of Dr.
Colton's series of related steroids were compared with
testosterone. Once again, norethandrolone came through
with flying colors. Dose for dose, it produced twice the
anabolic effect of testosterone.

After additional animal tests had proved that even massive
doses of norethandrolone were non-toxic, the new drug
was given the brand name Nilevar, and submitted to
numerous, qualified clinical investigators for therapeutic
evaluation of its tissue-building activity on humans.

Dr. Raymond E. Weston and his co-workers on the
Cardiovascular and Metabolic Research Service of New
York's Montefiore Hospital administered Nilevar to a series
of nutritionally depleted cardiac patients. Within twenty-
four to forty-eight hours they began to gain weight without
the fluid retention that often complicates cases of chronic
congestive heart failure.

At the Homer G. Phillips Hospital in St. Louis, Drs.

Joseph C. Peden, Mays Maxwell, and Alexandre Ohin conducted a controlled study on women who had just undergone extensive abdominal surgery. Those who received Nilevar excreted less nitrogen and achieved more rapid recoveries than the control patients, and did not develop any symptoms of masculinization.

Following stomach surgery for the removal of ulcers, many patients develop severe states of malnutrition, often losing as much as 10 percent of their pre-operative weight before slowly turning the corner toward recovery. To forestall such weight losses and hasten recovery Drs. Marion Hargrove, Alfredo Saravia, and Julian Ruffin administered Nilevar to a series of patients after gastrectomies at the Duke University Medical Center. In just one month of such therapy weight gains averaging more than eleven pounds were scored by the test group.

In another study, conducted by a team headed by Dr. Robert N. Watson, fifty-four chronically underweight men and women were divided into groups. At the end of twelve weeks those who received Nilevar had gained an average of five pounds, while those who unknowingly swallowed only inert placebo tablets gained an average of less than five ounces. Then, for the next twelve weeks, Nilevar was substituted for the inert tablets. This time the former placebo-takers, though unaware of the switch, gained an average of nearly six pounds. Since psychological factors, such as the enthusiasm of participating in the experiment, were thus ruled out, Nilevar's effectiveness in inducing weight gains was clearly established. "Androgenic effects such as hirsutism and voice changes were not observed," the clinical research team reported. "The only gastrointestinal symptom noted by any of the subjects was an increase of appetite."

Pediatricians Samuel S. Brown, Hersh W. Libo, and Arnold Nussbaum of the Jewish Hospital of Brooklyn studied eighty-six children brought to treatment because of persistent failure to gain weight. Under Nilevar therapy these youngsters scored consistent increases in their rate of weight gain. "Most patients," the investigators noted, "also exhibited an improvement in appetite, color, sleeping habits, vitality, and temperament."

A similar study of seventy nervous and underweight children was conducted by Dr. Louis S. Goldstein, Director of Pediatrics of the Yonkers Professional Hospital. While receiving Nilevar, every one of these patients achieved substantial weight increases, in some cases upward of ten pounds. "Our findings," Dr. Goldstein wrote in the *Archives of Pediatrics*, "support previous reports that norethandrolone possesses an exceedingly small androgenic activity and therefore is safe for administration in children. On the basis of our observations in this study, we are employing norethandrolone almost routinely to hasten the convalescence of hospitalized children."

In 1956, after numerous other studies had confirmed both its effectiveness as a protein-tissue-building agent and its low androgenicity, Nilevar was approved by the Federal Food and Drug Administration for use on prescription. And as, with experience, physicians gained confidence in the new steroid, they applied it in ever widening clinical fields: to hasten the healing of fractures, in the treatment of the bone disease osteoporosis, in arresting and reversing such disturbances of metabolism as calciuria, in preventing breakdowns caused by corticosteroid therapy, and in preparing debilitated patients for elective surgery.

Then, in December of 1958, the new anabolic agent was put to its severest and most dramatic test after a holocaust swept through Our Lady of the Angels School in Chicago, killing ninety-five children and teachers. Of the survivors, thirty-three horribly burned youngsters were rushed to the Franklin Boulevard Community Hospital. There, working desperately around the clock, physicians managed to save the lives of all but one. But once they had passed their initial crises, all of these youngsters began to exhibit the typical depletion of protein tissues generally experienced by victims of severe burns.

Traditionally, in such cases, physicians have prescribed diets high in proteins, calories, vitamins, and minerals. But the appetite of many burn victims is so impaired that they are unable to consume and absorb such optimal diets. Thus for all but two of the Chicago fire patients, Dr. William J. Kroulik, Medical Director of the Community Hospital, also prescribed Nilevar.

Eight of the most severely burned were given this anabolic steroid for three to nine weeks. All eight developed voracious appetites and gained from five to fifteen pounds during therapy. Their average gain in weight, over that recorded at the time of their admission, exceeded 14 percent. In sharp contrast, one of the children who did not receive norethandrolone lost two pounds during six weeks in the hospital, while the other gained only two pounds over a twelve-week period of hospitalization.

In his report in the *Journal of the International College of Surgeons*, Dr. Kroulik declared that Nilevar's "value to victims of extreme burns has been confirmed; it promoted a gain in weight in patients treated for three or more weeks and seemed to promote a feeling of well-being. In addition . . . the healing of wounds in the treated patients took place more rapidly than in the two patients who were not given the drug. . . ."

• • •

While surgeons, pediatricians, gerontologists, and general practitioners were thus welcoming Nilevar as a therapeutic tool of inestimable value, the hormone scientists who had created this tissue-rebuilding steroid were not content to regard it as the ultimate word in its field. Far from abandoning their steroid-screening program after their discovery of norethandrolone, biologists at the Searle research laboratories stepped up their efforts in order to assay the anabolic activity of all the new steroid compounds—approximately eight hundred a year—being synthesized by the laboratories' chemists.

One of the youngest and most junior of these chemists was Dr. Raphael Pappo. After winning his master's degree and his doctorate in organic chemistry at Israel's famed Weitzmann Institute, he had collaborated with Professor William S. Johnson at the University of Wisconsin on explorations of the total synthesis of steroids. When he joined the Searle staff late in 1956, his principal assignment concerned the synthesis of compounds related to the corticosteroid aldosterone. But when he wished to pursue a pet project of his own devising, Drs. Byron Riegel and Frank B. Colton arranged for him to have the necessary time and facilities.

"My idea," Dr. Pappo recalls, "was to see what would happen if I could manage to replace one of the carbon atoms of the central steroid nucleus with an atom of another element. Up until then, many chemists, myself included, had *assumed* that if you altered the nucleus you wouldn't have a steroid anymore; you'd completely destroy all steroid activity. But once I'd thought of the idea, it seemed silly to just go on *assuming*. I *had* to find out; it became a matter of satisfying a scientific curiosity.

"It turned out that it wasn't too difficult to replace the carbon atom at position number 2. So, I made this shift—from carbon to oxygen—on one of the simplest steroids. It was given a serial number, Searle Compound 8489, and it went over to the biology labs for activity tests.

"When I saw the test results, I was awfully disappointed, because 8489 had hardly any activity at all. But Dr. Riegel and Dr. Colton looked at it differently. What they saw was just that little bit of activity; that an oxy-steroid was still a steroid after all. And they encouraged me to go ahead and make higher steroids with an oxygen atom at the number-2 position. So we began to work up these compounds and, in 1959, we made SC-11585 which was similar to methyl-testosterone, except for the number-2 oxygen atom and a hydrogen atom attached to the number-5 carbon.

"When Drs. Saunders and H. D. Lennen put this new compound through biological tests, it had little effect on the weight of either the rats' semenal vesicles or the levator ani; by injection it showed only about one percent of the activity of testosterone. But, fortunately, they were real scientists and didn't stop there. When they tested it on rats by the oral route, it had no androgenic effect on the semenal vesicles and the prostate; but it had a whopping anabolic effect on the weight of the levator ani muscle. SC-11585 seemed to be just what we had all been looking for: an orally effective steroid with an even greater separation of effects than Nilevar."

But would this novel compound show the same low androgenicity and the same high anabolic activity on humans? To answer this crucial question, tablets of SC-11585 (given the generic name of oxandrolone) were sent to Dr. Grant W. Liddle, Associate Professor of Medicine and Director of Endocrinology at the Vanderbilt School of Med-

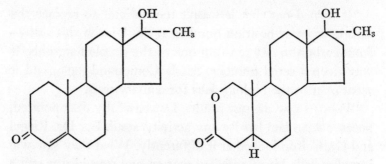

At left, a diagram of the chemical structure of methyltestosterone. At right, SC-11585; Anavar ®. The seemingly slight changes in the chemical structure of this new steroid—especially the introduction of an oxygen atom in the first ring—produces a sixfold increase in anabolic activity.

icine. There, together with Drs. Maurice Fox and Ann S. Minot, Dr. Liddle assayed the anabolic activity of the new steroid on a series of volunteers, by measuring the decline of their excretion of nitrogen after they swallowed the tablets. At various dosage levels oxandrolone's anabolic potency was found to be six times that of methyltestosterone or from two to three times that of Nilevar.

Over the next four years oxandrolone was subjected to even more extensive clinical studies than Nilevar had undergone. To provide a preliminary evaluation of its range of usefulness, 71 clinical investigators throughout the United States administered the new anabolic agent to 272 patients as part of their treatment of 47 distinct diagnoses. They noted improvements in over 70 percent of their patients. Many investigators also made intensive studies of the protein-building effects of oxandrolone—in postoperative states, in the aged, in chronically underweight children and adults, in sufferers from osteoporosis, and to offset catabolism associated with corticoid therapy.

Thus in 1964 the Federal Food and Drug Administration approved the marketing of oxandrolone under the brand name Anavar as a prescription drug for use under the supervision of physicians. Contraindications are few. Pending further studies, physicians do not prescribe it for patients with certain types of cancer nor for pregnant women or those who may become pregnant while under therapy. They use it only with great caution on patients with impaired liver function. And they give it with care to patients with certain cardiac or kidney diseases.

In therapy Anavar provides marked advantages over earlier tissue-building agents. Its high anabolic activity makes possible its use in oral doses as small as 2.5 milligrams and thus substantially reduces the cost of medication. Its minimal androgenic activity not only permits its use in the treatment of women and of youngsters of both sexes; it also allows the physician to adapt dosages more readily to the individual patient's needs. Where rapid rebuilding of tissues is considered essential, as for example in victims of extensive burns, physicians may prescribe as much as 10 milligrams a day or more, without fear of masculinizing side effects.

New and wider uses for Anavar are, in fact, rapidly being explored by clinical researchers. In this country, for example, a number of physicians have reported gratifying gains in height, without premature bone maturation, among children whose growth has been retarded. In a number of European countries physicians have been freely prescribing oxandrolone as a tissue rebuilder to relieve the debilitating effects of influenza or even of colds.

6

•

——————————————

TAMING THE RUNAWAY

STEROID

——————————————

•

When, in the late 1930s, Edward Kendell, Tadeus Reichstein, and Oscar Wintersteiner were isolating one adrenal hormone after another, they were all mystified by the same puzzling phenomenon.

From their original adrenal gland extracts they had crystallized a swarm of steroid substances, including six highly active hormones. The residue was a mother liquor they called "the amorphous fraction," because they could crystallize nothing more out of it. In theory it should have been totally lacking in hormonal activity. But when they tested it on dogs whose adrenals had been removed, it proved to be far more potent, in certain respects, than the most active of the hormones they had isolated.

Such adrenalectomized dogs, for example, had lost their ability to retain normal amounts of life-preserving sodium. But if the amorphous fraction was administered to these dogs, they no longer poured sodium out through their urine; they retained just as much of it as if their adrenal glands were still intact. In this country and in Switzerland the hormone hunters referred repeatedly in their reports to the surprising potency of this amorphous fraction, a clear indication that it still contained at least one powerful hormone they had not yet managed to flush out and identify.

Every corticoid-research group put down the isolation of this hormone as a high priority problem, to be attacked just as soon as they could get around to it. But then World War II began, and all of these research teams were sidetracked into the search for the mythical steroid supposedly helping Nazi pilots to fly higher than our own. And after that futile hunt ended they were diverted once again—this time by the unexpected discovery of cortisone's arthritis-relieving power and by the pressing race to overcome the ensuing cortisone famine. Thus, in the end, the mystery of the missing hormone was solved, not by the long-experienced adrenal-research teams but by two young scientific workers, who were comparative newcomers to steroid research.

At London's Middlesex Hospital and Medical School, in 1948, James Tait was a newly appointed, twenty-two-year-old Lecturer in Medical Physics. He had a tiny office and a

makeshift laboratory located in an out-of-the-way base-
ment corner. Sylvia Simpson, who later became Mrs. Tait,
was a research assistant, six floors up and nearly a block
away, in the biological laboratory. Both had full-time jobs.
Thus, only in the evenings and on weekends were they free
to pursue the project that really fascinated them: a study
of the mystifying mechanisms which control the salt-and-
water balance in our bodies. They had no grants and no
funds to finance their research; their only source of steroids
was a few vials of an adrenal extract called Eucortin, then
being marketed for clinical use by the British firm, Allen
and Hanburys.

Despite all these handicaps, however, they set out to accomplish what no one else had yet been able to. First they
taught themselves how to separate various hormone frac-
tions from their small supply of adrenal extract, using a
new method of paper chromatography developed by their
equally young biochemist friend, Ian Bush. Next, Jim Tait
prepared a mixture of radioactive sodium and potassium
which Sylvia Simpson fed to laboratory animals whose
adrenals she had removed. Then they administered one or
another of their hormone substances to these animals and
collected the urine excreted by each animal. Measurement
of the urine's radioactivity gave them extremely sensitive
assays of the salt-retaining effectiveness of each of the
adrenal hormones.

It took nearly three full years to perfect these delicate
techniques. But by late 1951 they had not only isolated an
adrenal hormone more active, in its salt-retaining activity,
than any previously known; they had also largely determined the chemical configuration of this steroid which they
tentatively named electrocortin.

The first reports of their work, published in the *Lancet*

and in *Nature* in the spring of 1952, were instantly recognized by older steroid researchers as the solution to the nagging mystery of the amorphous fraction. And from then on poverty no longer handicapped their work. Sir Charles Dodds, Britain's grand old man of steroid research, helped arrange for Tait and Miss Simpson to be released, in part, from their routine teaching and laboratory tasks. Even more important, he helped them set up a collaborative research program with the great steroid research teams of Tadeus Reichstein and Albert Wettstein in Switzerland.

Within less than a year they had established the full structure of the new hormone which they renamed aldosterone, because, uniquely among steroids, it had an aldehyde group of atoms as one of its side chains. Only six months later the co-operating groups perfected a method of synthesizing aldosterone.

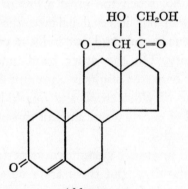

Aldosterone

Now, for the first time, it became clear to physiologists how our bodies maintain a stable, life-preserving balance of salts and water in their tissues, despite erratic and unpredictable changes in our environment that repeatedly tend to destroy that balance. A rise in surrounding temperature or the exertion of work, for example, may cause substantial quantities of water and salt to be poured out through our pores in the form of perspiration. A sudden drop in temperature may close down our pores and dam up our normal water-losing mechanisms. Thirst may impel us to ingest large quantities of water in a very short period, unaccompanied by balancing salt. Or, in a single meal, we may take in so much salt with our food that our sodium-water balance would shift way over in the opposite direction.

If we are in normal health, however, none of these sudden changes seriously affects us. Instead our kidneys, by continually adjusting the rate at which we excrete salts and water in urine, serve as vigilant guardians of our internal fluid and mineral balance. But our kidneys in turn are largely under the control of aldosterone secreted by our adrenal glands. So, when too great a loss of salt or water begins to threaten our internal balance, the adrenal steps up its aldosterone output and our kidneys cut down their excreting activity. On the other hand, any threatening overload of salt or water results in a prompt decrease of the adrenal's release of aldosterone and our kidneys are thus freed to get rid of excess water and salt through an increase in their urine output.

This sensitive automatic system works perfectly for most of us most of the time. But there are a number of conditions under which it fails, with disastrous results. For reasons not yet fully understood, cirrhosis of the liver, nephrosis or degeneration of kidney function, and a number of types of heart disease are often accompanied by a marked disturbance of adrenal function—and particularly by an increase in the output of aldosterone—which brings on a vicious cycle of increasingly massive salt-and-water retention. As a result, the tissues and body cavities of many victims of these diseases literally become waterlogged. This growing accumulation of fluids, known as edema, in turn greatly complicates the original maladies from which such patients suffer. Often, in fact, its effects prove more crippling, and even more deadly, than the underlying major illness.

Long before aldosterone was discovered, of course, physicians had recognized the need to relieve edema if they were to preserve the lives of their patients. As far back as the eighteenth century, British surgeons had developed a device with which they made a series of small cuts in the flesh of the legs so that they might drain off excess fluid brought to these extremities by gravity. Later there was the development of an emergency procedure, known as paracentesis, in which the abdominal or chest cavities of edematous patients were punctured with long hollow needles through which excess fluid could be drawn off.

Down through the centuries all sorts of potions have been used as diuretics to relieve edema. In fact digitalis, still one of our most effective heart-stimulating drugs, was originally used in 1785, not for its primary action upon the heart but because it seemed to exert a notable diuretic effect. It was not until the 1920s, however, that the first really effective treatment of edema became available with the discovery, by Dr. Albert Vogl, of the diuretic power of organic mercurial compounds. Still widely used today, these drugs have prolonged the lives of countless sufferers from edema.

Even more effective have been another group of drugs, the thiazides, first introduced in the late 1940s. Yet despite their value, these newer diuretics also had major drawbacks. While they substantially increased water and sodium excretion, they also often caused a simultaneous loss of potassium; sometimes so massive a loss of this essential mineral as to throw the patients into a deep and sometimes disastrous coma. Even when such dangerous side effects were not experienced, many patients treated with either the mercurial or the thiazide diuretics ultimately became "fast" to these drugs; the stimulation of their urine excretion proved only temporary and their edematous state redeveloped in form more extreme than before.

But with the discovery that the runaway overproduction of aldosterone was a major *immediate* cause of edema, alert researchers recognized that new possibilities for the control of edema had suddenly been opened up.

One approach, attempted in a number of laboratories, involved a search for compounds that might depress the adrenal glands' production of aldosterone. Several substances capable of exerting this effect were indeed discovered. Unfortunately, these chemicals also depressed the production of other essential adrenal cortex hormones and thus tended to upset many of the body functions normally regulated by the adrenals. Because of these dangerous "side effects," clinicians soon found the adrenal-depressing compounds much too disturbing to justify their use for the relief of edema.

A completely different approach to the problem, however, was taken by scientists at the Searle research laboratories. Instead of trying to reduce the excess production of aldosterone by the adrenals, they planned to attack this runaway steroid at another point, and began to search for compounds capable of keeping excess aldosterone from exerting its water-and-salt retaining effects upon the tiny tubules of the kidneys.

The idea that one compound might exert such a "blocking" action against another was not, of itself, new. Biochemists call such substances *competitive inhibitors*, meaning that they locate themselves upon a site, within some organ of the body, and thus inhibit another compound from acting upon that site. As far back as the early 1900s, in fact, the biochemist Paul Ehrlich, who had been awarded the Nobel Prize for his discovery of Salvarsan—the first effective drug used against syphilis—described the process of

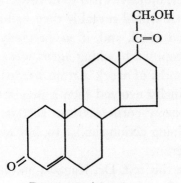

Desoxycorticosterone

competitive inhibition with a simple analogy. Suppose, he said, that the site of action is like the lock on a door and imagine the substance that acts on this site to be a perfectly fitting key. Then, if you wanted to fix it so that this key *couldn't* open the lock, one way to accomplish your purpose would be to insert into the keyhole another very similar, but not identical, key. Your new key wouldn't be able to open the lock. But as long as it was in the keyhole, the proper key would be blocked from entering. The result: competitive inhibition.

At that time, 1954, there was no precedent to suggest that competitive inhibition against a steroid molecule was possible. But at staff research conferences Searle's small band of steroid scientists decided that a systematic search for an aldosterone antagonist, or blocking agent, would be well worth while. To fit into the "keyhole" at aldosterone's site of action in the kidneys' tubules, the agent they were seeking would almost certainly have to be another steroid with a structure fairly similar to that of aldosterone.

Before the search for this hypothetical steroid could begin, however, biologists had to devise a method of testing compounds that would reveal if they had any aldosterone-blocking action at all, and, if so, precisely how strong an action each proposed blocking agent was capable of exerting. After months of work a team headed by Dr. Charles M. Kagawa finally evolved such a precise test. It involved the use of desoxy-corticosterone acetate, a steroid with a sodium-retaining action similar to, but much milder than, that of aldosterone.

To perform this test, Dr. Kagawa and his associates first removed the adrenal glands of laboratory rats so that they could no longer produce natural salt-retaining steroids. Into these rats the biologists injected accurately measured amounts of desoxycorticosterone acetate, called DOCA for short, and were thus able to control the amount of water and salt the test animals excreted in their urine. Then, by injecting *both* DOCA and any proposed blocking agent into their rats, they were able to discover whether or not the new substance blocked the action of DOCA and altered salt excretion. If it sufficiently increased the urinary output of sodium—without simultaneously increasing the output of potassium—it would be a potentially useful blocking agent.

Once this testing procedure was perfected, it became

possible to screen large numbers of steroids, one or more of which might prove capable of serving as a blocking agent. No one, of course, could predict how many compounds would have to be screened nor even whether an active aldosterone antagonist would ever be found. But human lives were at stake and the scientists had no choice but to go ahead—and hope.

By this time Searle's chemists had already synthesized several thousand steroid substances. Among these was one that had been prepared by Dr. John A. Cella in 1953, more than a year before the chemical structure of aldosterone

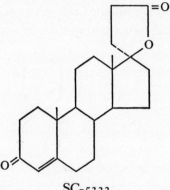

SC-5233

had been determined. Dr. Cella had synthesized it as one of a long series of compounds he was preparing in the hope of improving upon the then available heart-stimulating drugs. But when it turned out to have no particular value as a heartbeat stimulator, it had been given a serial number, Searle Compound 5233, and laid aside.

But SC-5233 did have a chemical configuration somewhat similar to that of the newly discovered aldosterone, and so it was included in the screening-program schedule. And when, early in 1956, its turn came to be subjected to the

Kagawa rat test, it proved to be exactly what the scientists had been seeking: an active aldosterone-blocking agent.

Like the mercurial diuretics, however, SC-5233 (which never was given another name) was found to be effective only when administered by injection. Thus Drs. Cella, Robert R. Burtner, Edward A. Brown, and Robert C. Tweit went back to their chemical laboratories and began trying to create an analog of SC-5233 that would be active when taken by mouth. One after another, new compounds were produced; one after another, these failed to demonstrate oral activity.

Then, after five months of hectic striving, they produced SC 8109, a steroid identical to SC 5233 except for the lack of one carbon and two hydrogen atoms on its number-19

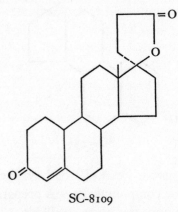

SC-8109

side chain. Yet, this minuscule difference in chemical structure effected a profound difference in anti-aldosterone activity. Biological tests soon demonstrated that it was at least two and a half times as active as its predecessor when injected. But much more important, it was also effective when administered orally.

After further animal tests had shown that both new compounds were not toxic at effective dosage levels, they were sent to Dr. Grant W. Liddle, Associate Professor of Medicine and Director of Endocrinology at the Vanderbilt University School of Medicine. Dr. Liddle tested them on dogs and found them quite as effective as the Kagawa tests had shown them to be on laboratory rats. Then he tried the new compounds on seven patients with varying degrees of edema due either to congestive heart failure or to nephrosis. In every instance the drugs induced a dramatic diuresis. The patients' abnormally low sodium excretion soared. But, unlike the other diuretics, the new steroids did not induce a simultaneous potassium loss.

Even while Dr. Liddle was conducting these preliminary tests on human volunteers, the chemists at the Skokie labs had been searching for a still more powerful anti-aldosterone compound. And in December, 1957, they produced SC-9420. In tests on rats it proved five times as effective orally as its predecessor; in clinical tests on human patients, the increase in activity was found to be nearly threefold. Here at last was a product worthy of a name. And since all of these aldosterone blockers belong to the spirolactone family of steroids, SC-9420—the most potent of all—was called Aldactone.

Now, both in the United States and abroad, the new steroid was supplied to numerous physician-researchers with long experience in the treatment of edema. Most of them selected, for their initial tests, the most challenging patients of all: those who had already received mercurial or thiazide therapy and upon whom these drugs had ceased to have any adequate diuretic effect. Time after time, in these desperately waterlogged patients, Aldactone effected a diuresis which other drugs no longer could.

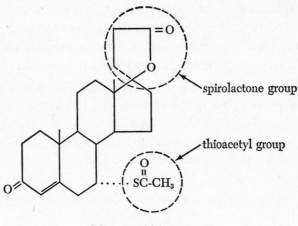

spirolactone group

thioacetyl group

SC 9420; Aldactone ®

At the University of Illinois Research and Education Hospitals, for example, Dr. Clarence L. Gantt used the new compound on twenty-seven victims of chronic liver disease, congestive heart failure, or nephrosis complicated by massive edema which had already become refractory to the conventional diuretics. In case after case Aldactone alone produced diuresis. In others the new spirolactone, in combination with a thiazide, brought about a diuresis that thiazide alone had proved no longer able to produce.

Among these patients the average weight loss through increased sodium-and-water excretion was thirty pounds. But one man, whose edema had run his weight up to 210 pounds, achieved a 60-pound weight loss and a complete disappearance of edema. In another instance nine days of thiazide therapy produced only a three-pound weight loss in a patient with severe congestive heart failure. Then Aldactone was added to his therapeutic regimen. In the next nine days the resulting excretion of water and sodium brought his weight down by twenty-seven pounds.

At Detroit's Henry Ford Hospital, Dr. John B. Bryan

used Aldactone on thirteen patients whose edema no longer responded to conventional diuretic therapy. In every one of these cases the new drug induced substantial salt-and-water excretion without dangerous potassium losses. In one dramatic instance, a cirrhotic patient achieved a weight loss of seventy-one pounds in an eighteen-day therapy period.

Similar results upon previously refractory states of edema were reported by Drs. Bernard F. Clowdus, John A. Higgins, John W. Rosevear, and William H. J. Summerskill of the Mayo Clinic; by Drs. Keith S. Henley, David H. P. Streeten, and H. Marvin Pollard of the University of Michigan Medical School; by Dr. Jacques Genest of Montreal's Hôtel-Dieu Hospital; by Drs. Liddle and W. S. Coppage of Vanderbilt University; by Dr. Robert S. Morrison of Boston's Lemuel Shattuck Hospital, and by numerous other clinical research teams.

By December of 1959, when the Federal Food and Drug Administration approved the marketing of Aldactone as a prescription drug, it was able to base that approval upon extended and detailed studies of literally thousands of victims of edema treated by more than two hundred clinical researchers.

One unexpected effect of Aldactone has been its ability to lower blood pressure in patients with hypertension. First noted in 1959 by Drs. William Hollander, Aram V. Chobanian, and Robert W. Wilkins of the Boston University School of Medicine, this property has since been confirmed by studies at the Cleveland Clinic Hospital conducted by Drs. A. J. Georgopoulos, Harriet Dustan, and Irvine H. Page; by Drs. W. J. Cranstan and B. E. Juel-Jensen of the Radcliffe Infirmary in Oxford, England, and by numerous other American, Canadian, and European researchers. The general use of Aldactone for the treatment of hypertension has not yet won FDA clearance in this country, although such use has been approved by drug-regulating authorities in Canada and a number of other countries.

The approval of Aldactone for use in the relief of edema was followed by its widespread adoption by both specialists and general practitioners to improve their treatment of patients with congestive heart failure, nephrosis, and hepatic cirrhosis. But since 1960 continued research has made available to physicians two even more effective forms of spironolactone steroids.

One was the result of a research feedback from clinical experimenters who had discovered that when they used Aldactone in combination with a thiazide, they could often achieve a much more rapid and profound relief of edema than when they used either preparation alone. Clinicians had also found that Aldactone offsets the potassium loss characteristically induced by the thiazide diuretics and thus protects patients from the dangers of comas and other grave consequences of potassium depletion. In 1961, therefore, a combination of Aldactone and hydrochlorthiazide was made available in a single pill, under the brand name Aldactazide.

Another major improvement resulted from the discovery that the absorption of spirolactone from the intestinal tract is much more complete if this steroid is prepared in the form of an extremely fine powder dispersed in a water-soluble matrix. Both laboratory and clinical studies revealed that a 25-milligram tablet of the much more finely ground drug produced an Aldactone blood level equivalent to that induced by a 100-milligram tablet of the older preparation. Thus, since 1962, physicians have had available two new products—Aldactone-A and Aldactazide-A—which permit them to prescribe much smaller daily doses with a consequent great reduction in the cost of the long-term treatment of edema.

While these improvements have helped win from physicians widespread recognition that the spironolactones represent one of the most effective and useful of all their weapons against edema, research, of course, has not ceased. At the Worcester Foundation for Experimental Biology, for example, Drs. James and Sylvia Tait—who first discovered aldosterone—have been painstakingly continuing their explorations of the manner in which this powerful steroid is metabolized in the bodies of both healthy and ill humans. In numerous other research centers and hospitals throughout the world, similar studies are also under way. And at the Searle laboratories a constant search is pursued for even more effective aldosterone antagonists.

7

THE SEARCH FOR

"THE PILL"

•

Through a long winter evening in 1950, a physician, a
biologist, and a nurse sat around a coffee table in a mid-
Manhattan apartment, far too involved in their discussion
to notice how late the hour had become.

The physician, and host, was Dr. Abraham Stone, one
of the gentlest, most soft-spoken, and most thoughtful of
men. Together with his beautiful and gifted wife Dr.
Hannah Stone, he had founded one of the world's first

fertility clinics, had helped thousands of infertile couples to achieve the pregnancies they so desperately wanted, and had taught thousands of others how to avoid the pregnancies which neither their health nor their finances could support. Since his wife's death ten years before, he had carried on this work, to which she had been so deeply devoted, and assumed added burdens as Clinical Professor of Preventive Medicine at New York University, as Editor of the *Journal of Human Fertility*, and as Medical Director and Vice-President of the Planned Parenthood Federation.

The biologist was Gregory Pincus, a scientist whose entire life had been directed toward the unraveling of the intricate mysteries of human and animal reproductive processes. Though ten years younger than his friend Abe Stone, "Goody" Pincus had long since won world-wide recognition as a leader in hormone research. For more than a dozen years his colleagues had re-elected him Chairman of their Laurentian Hormone Conference and Editor of its definitive annual, *Progress in Hormone Research*. And since its establishment in 1944, he had been co-director of the Worcester Foundation for Experimental Biology, from which had emerged a stream of fundamental advances in science's unending battles against cancer, mental illness, and the complex disorders of the reproductive organs.

The nurse was Margaret Sanger, fiery founder of the Planned Parenthood movement. Time after time, as a young public health worker climbing the stairs of fetid tenements in New York's Lower East Side, she had witnessed the agonies of desperate mothers who had attempted abortions upon themselves because they could not bear the thought of adding still another child to their hungry broods. Despite all she tried to do for them, many had died of massive hemorrhages or rampant uterine infections. And she had come to wonder whether those whose lives she had helped to save had really been helped at all, since both custom and law forbade her teaching these poor women how to protect themselves against still another pregnancy—and then another. When, at last, she could no longer contain her indignation, Mrs. Sanger had boldly opened this country's first contraceptive clinic in the Brooklyn slum of Brownsville, and proudly braved arrests and jail sentences to challenge the law's cruel prohibition.

Now, after thirty-eight years, her crusade had won scores of thousands of supporters. More than a hundred Planned Parenthood Clinics dotted the land. Millions were using the contraceptive methods she and her medical associates had introduced and developed. But though her struggle had changed in form, it was unfinished and she was determined to see it through to a final victory. Thus, during the discussion that evening, she was just as earnest, as hard-driving, as vehement as when her long battle had first begun.

"It has been more than a dozen years since the police have raided and closed down any of our clinics," she said. "Month after month, more thousands of women than ever before are coming to our centers to learn about birth control. In their own offices, thousands of doctors are to-day teaching contraceptive methods to their patients. But the trouble now is that these methods just aren't good enough. They only reduce the risk of pregnancy, they don't eliminate it."

Then, addressing her words to Dr. Pincus, she added brusquely, "It's high time you scientists did something to end this disgraceful situation."

Before Pincus could reply, Abe Stone spoke up. "Margaret," he chided, "don't scold my friend. He knows it's high time."

Then, walking over to his paper-piled desk, the physician picked up a time-faded medical journal. "Let me read you something that Hannah and I wrote fifteen years ago—a sort of prescription. 'The ideal contraceptive still remains to be developed. It should be harmless . . . entirely reliable . . . simple, practical, universally applicable, and esthetically satisfactory to both husband and wife.' "

"That's why I made you come down here, Goody." Stone continued. "Friends of the Planned Parenthood Federation have raised a little money—not much, just enough to get research for more effective birth control methods started. Our Research Committee has already allotted most of this fund to the improvement of present methods, to the development of better diaphragms or sperm-killing jellies and creams. But I've insisted that this isn't enough. We've got to get original research under way, based on new ideas, aimed at a new kind of breakthrough; the kind of research that only people like yourself will be able to carry on. How about it? We can put in a little money. Will you put up your brains and your time?"

Solemn-faced and seemingly resisting, Pincus sat silent for several moments. Then his eyes twinkled and a smile lit up his face. "If both of you hadn't talked so long," he told them, "I'd have said yes twenty minutes ago."

It was not until the next day, on his long drive home to Worcester, that Dr. Pincus began to realize what he had let himself in for.

He was already involved in a half dozen research projects which couldn't be put aside. Now he would have to find some way of assigning much of this work to his associates and assistants.

The Foundation's share of the Planned Parenthood Research Fund had turned out to be only $2,100—barely enough to pay for the rabbits they would need in the first few months of experiments.

To finance the work adequately, even for just one year, he would have to raise an additional twenty to thirty thousand dollars. And how could he know that it wouldn't take three years to come up with anything worthwhile— or five—or even ten?

But he had put himself in such boxes before—and worked his way out of them. Besides, this project was far too intriguing, its potential benefits for humanity far too great to permit mere money worries to get in its way. Better just to forget about finances, for the moment, and begin thinking about how to tackle the research.

All of the conventional contraceptives depended upon setting up a mechanical or chemical barrier to prevent male sperm cells from reaching the female ovum or egg cell. All too often they failed, because these barriers just were not good enough. But even improved barrier contraceptives would also frequently fail, because they would still have to be utilized at just the right time by preoccupied, fallible humans.

But what about preventing conception *without* using a barrier method? What about a *physiological* approach to the problem? Would it be possible to develop some drug that would make either the male or the female temporarily infertile? Suppose, for example, you could devise a simple, safe, absolutely reliable pill that would keep a woman from ovulating? If she had no egg, no mechanical or chemical barrier to prevent fertilization would be needed.

But wait a minute. Doesn't nature already do just that in every normal pregnancy? As soon as a fertilized ovum begins to grow in the womb, doesn't it step up the output of one of the female sex hormones—progesterone? And doesn't this in turn cause the ovaries to cease maturing and releasing additional ova throughout the entire period of pregnancy?

Well then, what about trying to use nature's method to suppress ovulation in non-pregnant women?

Progesterone was non-toxic and therefore safe to use as a drug. In fact, physicians had been giving massive injections of it for many years, as a means of preventing threatened miscarriages among so-called "habitual aborters" who didn't produce enough natural progesterone to maintain a pregnancy through to completion.

But painful, expensive injections would never do for contraceptive purposes. An ideal physiological contraceptive would have to be something taken by mouth. That's where the research would have to start. The very first move would be to find out whether progesterone would retain its ovulation-inhibiting power if it were orally administered.

The ride back to Worcester was almost over now. But Goody Pincus was far too excited to go right home. Instead he drove straight to the Foundation labs which were about to close for the day. And all that evening he and his co-director Hudson Hoagland, and Senior Scientist Min-Chueh Chang, their long-time associate, discussed and dissected and criticized the idea of a physiological oral contraceptive, and hammered out the experimental design of their research. The next morning that research got under way.

As a first step, Pincus and Chang fed varying amounts of progesterone to female rabbits. Twenty-four hours later they put these females with males in mating cages. Those that had received less than two milligrams of progesterone continued, rabbit-like, to multiply, producing large, normal litters. Among those that got slightly larger doses, only a few became pregnant. And among those whose oral dose had exceeded five milligrams—still barely enough to cover the head of a pin—ovulation was completely halted and not one became pregnant.

From rabbits they turned to laboratory rats, which normally ovulate in cycles similar to (though shorter than) those of humans. First they studied some five dozen untreated females, which had been placed in mating cages with provenly fertile male rats; the females became pregnant within slightly less than five days on the average.

Then a second group of five dozen more females were put through the same routine, but only after they had been fed five to fifty milligrams of progesterone—about as much as half a pinch of salt. This time, mating had to be allowed to proceed for more than ten days, on the average, before pregnancy occurred. The single tiny dose of progesterone was sufficient to suppress ovulation for at least one full cyclic period.

Here was the answer to the first crucial question. Progesterone was indeed active as an ovulation inhibitor when administered orally—at least on laboratory rats and rabbits.

But would it work in the same way on humans?

While these animal experiments were being carried out

in Worcester, another gifted researcher, less than forty miles away, was independently tackling a vastly different problem. At the Free Hospital for Women in the Boston suburb of Brookline, Harvard's professor of gynecology John Rock was director of one of the country's best and busiest fertility clinics. Like others of the small, skilled band of fertility specialists, Rock had succeeded in relieving the barrenness of an increasing percentage of women whose failure to bear children could be identified with a specific cause. But, again like all the rest of his colleagues, he was stymied by case after case in which no single cause of infertility could be named and indicted. To these anxious supplicants he could offer only the tissue-thin hope that trial-and-error treatments—plus a great dose of good luck —might lead to a yearned-for pregnancy.

Studying the records of hundreds of such patients, Rock had noted that a large proportion of them seemed to be victims of hypoplasia—an underdevelopment of the ovarian tubes or the uterus. He knew that in normal women the start of pregnancy—and the resulting sharp rise in the output of the female sex hormones, estrogen and progesterone—produced a marked increase in the size of both the tubes and the uterus. "In the absence of real pregnancy," Dr. Rock asked himself, "might not the administration of these hormones bring about a pseudopregnancy that would stimulate the growth of the tubes and the womb, correcting their dysfunction and making fertilization and pregnancy possible?"

To one after another of his inexplicably infertile patients John Rock explained both his theory and the fact that it was only a theory. Previous widespread use of both hormones for the relief of other conditions had demonstrated that what he proposed to do would surely be harmless. But the treatment, he emphasized, would be completely experimental. He could promise nothing except the shadow of a hope that it might just possibly prove helpful.

Despite the doctor's deliberate and calculated pessimism, eighty frustrated but valiantly adventuresome women, all of whom had been futilely seeking motherhood for from two to six years, volunteered to cooperate in the experiments. Daily for three months they swallowed increasingly larger doses of the synthetic estrogen, diethylstilbestrol, and similarly increasing doses of progesterone. Exactly as Dr. Rock had warned, they developed pseudopregnancies that seemed all too real. They suffered nausea indistinguishable from the morning sickness of the pregnant; their breasts became enlarged and tender, their nipples tingled and became pigmented; they missed first one menstrual period and then another. Their husbands, though warned that these false signs of pregnancy might appear, frequently had to be reminded that they were *not* becoming fathers and reassured that their wives were *not* being injured by the treatments.

Over a period of eighteen months, as one woman after another completed her three-month course of hormone-taking, these reassurances were confirmed by the prompt return of these women to their normal menstrual cycles. In sixty-seven cases, in fact, that was all that happened.

But in thirteen other instances—several times as many as could possibly be accounted for by chance—the women became pregnant within four months or less after treatment had been discontinued. Rock's inspired guess that a "rebound reaction" might occur had brought the all but despaired of happiness of parenthood to these thirteen once "hopeless" cases.

The emotional shock that both wives and husbands seemed to suffer when the treatments suppressed menstruation, however, convinced Dr. Rock that the time had come to discontinue his bold experiment and search for some less drastic way of accomplishing the same end.

Fortunately, just at this time, chance brought the two old friends, Pincus and Rock, together at a scientific conference. Between sessions, they exchanged details of what each had been doing since their last meeting. Thus, when Rock embarked upon a new attempt to evoke the rebound reaction, he used progesterone alone. And to avoid the possibility of the objectionable suppression of menstruation, he instructed his patients—at Dr. Pincus' suggestion—to interrupt their medication after twenty days and not to resume taking the progesterone pills until the fifth day after their menstrual periods began.

This time twenty-seven barren women, who had been infertile for more than two years, volunteered for the treatments. For a month, during which she took no medication, each woman was kept under close observation at Dr. Rock's newly established Reproductive Study Center across the street from the Free Hospital. A study of temperature curves, uterine biopsies, and vaginal smears proved that each ovulated in normal fashion.

Only when this fact was thoroughly established did the various patients begin their oral dosing with progesterone, starting on the fifth day after the beginning of their menstrual period. During the month, each patient again reported for the various tests. But now these tests indicated that almost all of them had ceased to ovulate. Yet none of these women experienced the pronounced pseudopregnancy symptoms of their predecessors. And when treatment was withdrawn after twenty days of taking the hormone, each volunteer promptly began to menstruate.

In this manner thirteen of the women went through two months of treatment and fourteen others continued the experiment for three full cycles, while Rock waited anxiously to see whether the new and far less emotionally disturbing regimen would again produce the hoped-for rebound reaction.

Considering the low fertility potential of all the women in this group, the occurrence among them of even a single pregnancy would have been something to crow about. But within four months after medication was stopped, John Rock found himself the prospective godfather of not one baby but four! And Dr. Pincus, with proof that progesterone *could* inhibit ovulation in humans as well as in laboratory animals, was able to plan further steps in his hunt for an effective oral fertility inhibitor.

Despite the success of this second fertility-fostering experiment, neither Dr. Rock nor Dr. Pincus was fully satisfied with the performance of progesterone. From Rock's viewpoint, as a fertility specialist, progesterone suffered from the great disadvantage of causing a slight bleeding or "premature menses" in some 20 percent of the treated monthly cycles. Even though these "breakthroughs" could be overcome by a prompt increase in dosage, their occurrence was highly disturbing to the patients. From Pincus' point of view, the fact that progesterone inhibited ovulation only about 85 percent of the time loomed as a major drawback to its potential mass use as a contraceptive. Worst of all, when administered orally, tremendous doses of progesterone were required to insure the suppression of ovulation.

What was obviously needed, both for Rock's purpose and for Pincus', was a compound as harmless as progesterone, but one that could be used in small, inexpensive doses and still invariably prevent both ovulation and breakthrough bleeding. Thus, in September of 1953, Dr. Pincus asked the major hormone-producing companies to send him samples of all the progesterone-like steroids that their chemists had ever synthesized.

More than two years earlier, at the Searle laboratories, a group of chemists under Dr. Byron Riegel had begun a search for compounds that would have progesterone's useful properties without its undesirable qualities. Progesterone, for example, was highly active when administered by injection. But any given dose taken orally exerted only a fraction of the potential activity of the same dose given as an injection. Thus one major objective of the Searle researchers was to find an analog of progesterone—a steroid of somewhat similar structural form—that would be far more active when taken orally. It would also, of course, have to exert minimal side effects and would have to be completely safe though used repeatedly over a long period of time.

One of the researchers working under Dr. Riegel was Dr. Frank Colton, who had received much of his experience in steroid chemistry as an assistant to Dr. Edward C. Kendall at the Mayo Clinic. In this new project he concentrated his attention upon the synthesis of what were called 19-nor steroids, which differ from such natural steroids as progesterone in that they lack a side chain of one carbon and three hydrogen atoms (a so-called methyl group) at the number-19 position. Eight years earlier Professor Maximilian Ehrenstein of the University of Pennsylvania had put together the first such compound, 19-nor progesterone, while seeking new heartbeat stimulating substances. It had not been useful for his purpose, but in a test on just two rabbits, he had observed that it had a progestational effect similar to that of progesterone. Since Professor Ehrenstein had used up his 19-nor compound, he merely noted this effect and let it go at that. Later, at the University of Wisconsin, Drs. Alfred L. Wilds and Norman A. Nelson developed an improved laboratory technique of making 19-nor progesterone.

To Drs. Colton and Riegel and Raymond, however, this seemed a clue clearly worth following up. So, in the summer of 1952, Dr. Colton began working out the synthesis of a whole series of 19-nor steriods. As each of these was put together, it was sent to Searle's Biological Research Division where Drs. Victor Drill and Francis J. Saunders and their co-workers put it through a long series of animal tests to determine whether it possessed any oral progestational activity, and to establish whether it was safe to use or toxic and whether its administration would evoke undesirable side effects. By December of 1952 these tests had revealed an unexpectedly high score for one of Dr. Colton's compounds, norethynodrel, which had been given the identification number SC-4642. A few months later another compound, SC-5914 or norethandrolone, also was found to possess a substantial number of the desired properties. Thus, both of these compounds were among the batch of samples promptly submitted by the Searle company for the projected Worcester screening tests.

Through the fall of 1953 the lights burned late in the laboratories at Worcester, as Dr. Chang, Dr. Pincus and what had now grown into a whole platoon of assisting scientists and technicians tested nearly two hundred compounds for ovulation-inhibiting potency upon a small army of rabbits and rats. By December the series of animal experiments were finally completed. Fifteen compounds had proved to have some effect as ovulation inhibitors. More important, three 19-nor steroids—norethisterone, SC-5914 or norethandrolone, and SC-4642 or norethynodrel (later named Enovid)—were found not only effective when administered orally but also much more active than proges-

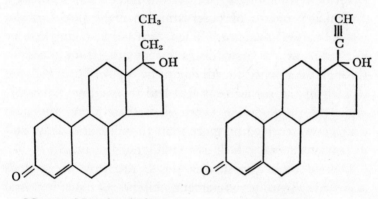

SC-5914; Norethandrolone   Norethisterone

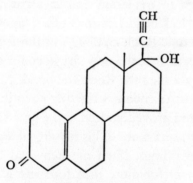

SC-4642; Norethynodrel

terone in suppressing ovulation in laboratory animals. Norethynodrel, in fact, had tested out as at least ten times as active as progesterone.

Now John Rock, aided by Drs. Luigi Mastroianni, Jr., John V. Kelly, and Celso Ramon Garcia (who left his post as assistant professor of obstetrics and gynecology at the University of Puerto Rico to join the Brookline team) began to recruit a new group of fifty infertile women for a third series of tests. Once again, each woman went through a preliminary month of observation to make sure that she was a "natural ovulator." Then each began taking one or the other of the new drugs by mouth, from the fifth through the twenty-fourth day of her cycle. But where the women in the earlier tests had had to swallow 300 milligrams of progesterone every day, those using the new drugs now received no more than 50 milligrams daily, and in some instances, as little as 10 milligrams a day.

Despite these far smaller doses, the new compounds achieved a virtually 100-percent inhibition of ovulation. And when the women completed their two-cycle or three-cycle courses of treatment, every last one promptly resumed her normal pattern of ovulation and menstruation, indicating that the drug had no deleterious effect upon their organs.

For a third time Rock sweated out the weeks of waiting for the first signs that the new drugs could evoke what his colleagues now called the Rock Rebound. After nearly two months his worries ended as the first ecstatic patient rushed to his offices and proved, indeed, to be pregnant. During the next few months six more of his fifty troubled women heard the same glad tidings. Two of them had been trying to become pregnant for more than four and a half years; another had been infertile for at least five years; still another achieved pregnancy after more than six years of hoping against hope.

Thus it became clear that these 19-nor steroids, and particularly norethynodrel, were not only valuable agents for the relief of difficult cases of infertility; they were also far more active than progesterone in inhibiting ovulation *in humans* and produced far fewer, and far milder, side effects than had occurred in the earlier progesterone experiments.

Nearly five years had passed since Dr. Pincus had begun —with just a hope, an idea, and a $2,100 grant—his hunt for a physiological means of contraception. Through a dozen unpredicted turnings that search had drawn in scores of other collaborators; chemists, biologists, pharmacologists, and clinical researchers. It had cost not $2,100 nor $21,000, but over $300,000.

Although orally active ovulation inhibitors had been developed, the project was far from completion. Far more extensive tests, not on just fifty women but on many hundreds and even thousands, would have to be conducted before scientists could be sure that "The Pill"—as they were already calling it—would be both effective and safe for long-term contraceptive use.

8

•

———————————

THE YEARS OF TESTING

———————————

•

Most of us tend to think of the gifted scientist as a man with a unique ability to find the answers to nature's riddles. Yet a far more important attribute of the truly brilliant scientist is the ability to ask the right questions. For unless all of the proper questions are asked, the most diligent, answer-seeking research will inevitably lead only up blind alleys.

Thus even while the Brookline experiments with the 19-nor steriods were under way, Gregory Pincus was worrying over the questions that would determine the ultimate design of a new set of experiments: the all-essential field trials which would reveal whether the new ovulation inhibitors could fully meet Dr. Stone's prescription for an ideal contraceptive, or fall far short of the mark.

Dr. Rock's fifty infertile women, for example, had had not the slightest thought of contraception when they willingly swallowed their 19-nor steriod pills. Exactly what they swallowed, in fact, hardly mattered to them at all. They would have accepted eagerly almost any drug that offered them a hope of overcoming their inability to achieve pregnancy. But would other women, seeking to avoid an unwanted pregnancy, find these steriods equally acceptable? Would they deliberately choose to use the pills when conventional contraceptives were available to them?

The fifty New England women had known that they would be taking the pills for only a few months. Would other women be willing to use them continuously—month after month after month, and possibly for years on end?

The Brookline patients were a select group: well-educated women who had no difficulty in following faithfully the regimen Drs. Pincus and Rock devised for them. But would women without educational advantages be able to follow a similar schedule and take the pills regularly, for precisely the prescribed number of days, without lapses? And if they did skip the pills for one day, or for two, or for three, what would happen to them?

And what about side effects? Would many women experience the mild nausea or the mild headaches that a few of Dr. Rock's patients had noted at the start of their therapy? Would such side effects persist through months of using the pills for contraceptive purposes? Would they grow more severe with continued use of the pills? Would new, more disturbing side effects appear among women who used the synthetic hormones over protracted periods?

Even more important: what about long-term effects—
on the blood, liver, kidneys, thyroid, adrenals, ovaries,
uterus, or other organs? Would prolonged use of the pills
endanger the health, or even the lives, of any of the women
who relied upon this physiological contraceptive? Were
there some women, in fact, who should not be allowed to
use the pills; women with a pre-existing condition, perhaps,
that the pills might exacerbate?

And what about women who would decide—after using
the new contraceptive for a year or two or three—that
they now wanted a child? Dr. Rock had found the pill's
ovulation-inhibiting effect reversible. When he ceased administering the 19-nor steriods to his infertile patients, they
had promptly resumed their normal patterns of ovulation.
But would this be true of women who used the pill for
many months or even years?

Not until all these and a host of similar questions could
be definitively answered, Dr. Pincus knew, would it be
proper in good conscience to make the new steroids available for general use as contraceptives. Thus he began to
search for an area where ovulation inhibitors could be subjected to extensive, rigorous, and carefully controlled field
trials involving first scores and then many hundreds of
volunteer pill-users.

Ideally, such an area would be one with a high birth rate,
where women married and began bearing children at an
early age, and where many thus would be anxious to halt
the growth of their families while they were still at the
height of their potential fecundity. Ideally, too, it should be
an area whose population included a fairly high proportion
of semi-literate or even illiterate women, so that the ability
of the educationally disadvantaged to follow pill-taking
schedules might be thoroughly tested. Ideally it should

be an area in which either poverty or custom had habituated women to a reliance upon public health workers rather than family doctors; for only in such an area would a truly representative sample of the general population of women be willing to make themselves available for examinations and interviews with field trial physicians and their aides. Finally, the site of the proposed field trials would have to be one in which circumstances minimized any tendency for volunteers to move away and thus be lost to follow-ups by doctors and social workers.

Dr. Pincus found such an area in Puerto Rico, where a tremendously high birth rate and a rapidly falling death rate—the result of excellent public health measures instituted by the Commonwealth government—had combined to make this beautiful island one of the most densely populated regions in the world. Here, among the very young, education was already eliminating illiteracy. But married couples, in their late twenties or early thirties, still included many who could read barely or not at all. And here, too, a determined, able, and energetic woman, Dr. Edris Rice-Wray, medical director of Puerto Rico's Family Planning Association, was willing to undertake the exacting and demanding task of supervising a series of prolonged mass experiments.

Thus, early in 1956, a low-income housing development in a slum clearance area at Rio Piedras, a suburb of San Juan, was selected for a preliminary field trial experiment in which procedures for enlisting, examining, and following up volunteer pill-users could be developed and thoroughly tested and, if necessary, modified and retested.

In the experiments at the Brookline Reproductive Study Center, three different synthetic steroids had been used for short-term suppression of ovulation. For the new field trials, however, it was felt to be essential to determine which of these promised to be most effective and safest for long-term use. Thus Dr. Pincus and his associates at the Worcester Foundation put all three compounds through a series of animal assay tests.

Norethynodrel—Searle Compound No. 4642—proved to be by far the most active in suppressing ovulation. Norethandrolone—Searle Compound No. 5914—and norethyndrone both were found to possess a mild androgenic, or potentially masculinizing, activity in contrast to the slightly estrogenic activity of norethynodrel. Since any masculinizing effect would be undesirable in a product intended for prolonged use by women, it was decided to use norethynodrel in the forthcoming field trials.

When this compound first was made at the Searle research laboratories, the production process introduced between one and two percent of an estrogenic "contaminant." Later, when this "contaminant" was removed, the pure 19-nor steroid had failed to prevent, in some women, what is known as spotting or breakthrough bleeding toward the end of the ovulation-inhibiting cycles. But when the "contaminant" estrogen, mestranol, was deliberately re-added to 10-milligram doses of the pure 19-nor steroid, breakthrough bleeding was again prevented. For this reason a second decision was made: norethynodrel *plus* 1.5 percent of mestranol would be used as standardized test pills in the field trials. It is this combination which has since become known throughout the world as Enovid® or *"the* pill."

In April, 1956, in the housing development at Rio Piedras, Dr. Rice-Wray and her aides began to visit women still less than forty years old who had already given birth to two or more children. Many had previously been given conventional barrier contraceptives at the Family Planning Association clinic, but they had either found their correct use difficult or had given them up because they doubted their efficacy. But as the grapevine carried the word from house to house that the "lady doctor" had a pill that could help women have only as many children as they could support and take care of, the interviewers were besieged by several times as many applicants as they were prepared to accept for the preliminary field trials.

The anxiety of these poor women to be included in the experiment was easy to understand. Typical was Julia A.— at thirty-one the mother of five children and the wife of a mentally-ill husband who would not consent to sterilization for himself or his mate. Felicia G. had even more reason to grasp eagerly for surcease from childbearing, for though she was but thirty years old, she was already the mother of ten children ranging in age from sixteen years to ten months; and because her husband was both ill and a heavy drinker, the major responsibility for supporting this brood fell to her.

Before any volunteer was accepted into the project, Dr. Celso Ramon Garcia—the gynecologist who had collaborated with Dr. Rock in the first clinical studies of the 19-nor steroids—gave her a complete physical examination, with particular attention to the pelvic organs and the breasts. Only those who evidenced no signs of ill health were given a small bottle containing twenty 10-milligram Enovid pills. Each was instructed to take only one pill a day, starting five days after the onset of her period. Following these directions, each would automatically discontinue medication on the twenty-fifth day of her cycle. Since she would then have to return to the clinic offices to obtain a new twenty-pill supply, the field workers were assured of an opportunity for a thorough interview each month and for a new physical examination if necessary.

Every woman was warned that she might experience nausea, vomiting, dizziness, abdominal pain, diarrhea, or other side effects. Yet despite this warning more than two hundred women enrolled themselves in the study. Thus, almost from the start of the trials, researchers got at least a tentative answer to one of their questions. Large numbers of women *would* willingly try the pills even though they had rejected or discarded other available contraceptives.

As it turned out, not all women were able to use the pills correctly and continuously. A few quit because their husbands objected; a few more dropped out on the advice of either their priest or a physician not associated with the project; a few moved away; and about twenty-five stopped taking the pills because they were frightened by the side effects which they had been warned might occur. One woman misunderstood the instructions and took the tablets only when her husband was not traveling. Another, after she became pregnant, complained that the pills hadn't worked at all even though she had made her husband take them every day. As each of these women was dropped from the test group, she was replaced by a new volunteer.

By January, 1957, when the preliminary trial records were reviewed, 221 women of proven fertility had taken Enovid for periods varying from one to nine full months, while they had continued to live with their husbands and had no recourse to any other method of birth control. But as long as they took the pills regularly, not a single one of these women had become pregnant. "The drug," Dr. Rice-Wray reported, "has given 100 percent protection against pregnancy in 10-milligram doses taken for twenty days each month."

Here again, the preliminary trials provided a tentative, affirmative answer to a key question. As long as the pills were correctly used, they were entirely reliable as contraceptives; more effective, in fact, than any previously available preparations or devices.

Among the dropouts, however, seventeen had become pregnant. But these "failures" provided at least a preliminary answer to one of Dr. Pincus' most important questions. Even though ovulation had been suppressed in these women for up to nine months, their fertility had obviously not been adversely affected.

As these results were analyzed, new rules of procedure were drawn up for the further field trials. From then on, in addition to the thorough initial physical examination, periodic vaginal and cervical cytological tests were instituted; blood samples were taken, and hemoglobin concentrations, clotting times, and leucocyte counts studied; protein bound iodine was measured in order to reveal any changes in thyroid function; numerous liver-function tests were performed.

Early in 1957 at Rio Piedras, Dr. Rice-Wray reopened her enrollment books and gradually accepted several hundred additional women who had been anxiously awaiting their chance to join the trials. In April, forty miles to the southeast in the small town of Humacao, a second large field trial got under way under the direction of Dr. Adeline Pendleton Satterthwaite, an obstetrician and gynecologist at the Ryder Memorial Hospital. A year later, in Port-au-Prince, Haiti, where poverty and illiteracy were far greater than in Puerto Rico, a third project was started under a research committee made up of Drs. Felix Laraque, Réné Nicolas, Raymond Borno, and Vergniaud Pean.

By 1960 more than sixteen hundred women at these Caribbean Field Trial Centers had used Enovid as a contraceptive for from a few months to nearly four years Their experience, as a group, with the new steroid covered nearly forty thousand menstrual cycles or—as medical statisticians prefer to put it—about three thousand woman-years of exposure to the possibility of pregnancy.

Prior to their enrollment in the field trials, these extremely fertile young women had been experiencing new pregnancies within an average of less than three months after childbirth. In statistical terms, their effective fertility rate had been 110 pregnancies per 100 women per year. But only forty-five pregnancies occurred among the volunteers during the field trials. The pregnancy rate for all the sixteen hundred-plus women in the field trials had dropped from 110.0 percent to only 1.6 percent!

Yet even this phenomenal reduction in pregnancies actually gave a distorted picture of Enovid's true effectiveness. For when the records of these cases were checked, it was found that in virtually every instance, these women had failed to take from one to as many as nineteen pills during the month in which they became pregnant. Save for these "accidents," the direct result of not following the pill-a-day regimen, Enovid had established a 100-percent record of effectiveness as a contraceptive.

During these same years, from 1957 onward, a number of other groups of clinicians also undertook experimental studies of the contraceptive utility of Enovid. At the Norfolk, Virginia, General Hospital, for example, Drs. William C. and Mason C. Andrews tested the steroid pills on 191 women for a total of 1,381 cycles. During this entire period, not a single one of these volunteers became pregnant. At the Fitzsimons Army Hospital, Dr. John Albert Morris, Jr., directed a fourteen-month test of Enovid as a contraceptive during which 97 Army wives used the pills through a total of 492 cycles without a single pregnancy.

Dr. Charles S. Mahan, Assistant Professor of Obstetrics at the West Virginia University School of Medicine, observed a group of a hundred women through eight hundred cycles of Enovid treatment. Once again, not one volunteer became pregnant while using the pills.

The most rigorous and extensive of all these studies was started in 1957 by Dr. Edward T. Tyler of the University of California School of Medicine. During a five-year period, at the Los Angeles Planned Parenthood Center, he supervised a field trial in which 562 women used Enovid for a total of 8,218 cycles without experiencing a single pregnancy.

"I must admit very frankly," Dr. Tyler declared at a 1961 Medical Symposium, "that our initial attitude toward the oral progestin method of conception control was one of skepticism. Dr. Pincus and I had many early differences of opinion concerning this method of conception control. But I will also confess that my opinion is continuously changing. The longer our studies proceed, and the more we see long-term users of these progestins, the more impressed we are with their effectiveness and their usefulness as a method of contraception."

In the short preliminary field trials at San Juan in 1956, approximately 17 percent of the volunteers complained of the occurrence of unpleasant side effects when they took Enovid. In the extended field trials, in Rio Piedras, in Humacao, and in Haiti, similar complaints were voiced by nearly a third of the volunteers *during their first month of using Enovid*. But in their second month "on the pills," more than half these women noted no recurrence of side effects. From then on only a tiny, ever decreasing fraction of all users had any complaints to report at their monthly interviews.

Undoubtedly some of these side effects were "real," for the pills do create a physiological state closely resembling early pregnancy. The drop-off in the occurrence of side effects also parallels what happens during pregnancy, since the nausea and vomiting of "morning sickness" usually ends as pregnancy advances.

But the field workers had been warning every new volunteer that she might experience side effects. They had often even indicated precisely what side effects could be expected. It was not surprising, therefore, that these women because acutely alert to any minor malaise or discomfort they would have ignored under other circumstances. Thus Dr. Pincus and Dr. Manuel Paniagua, who had succeeded Dr. Rice-Wray as medical director of the Family Planning Association, suspected that at least some portion of the side effects reported by the volunteers were derived from psychological rather than physiological causes.

To check this hypothesis they initiated a three-way experiment. To one small group of new volunteers, Dr. Paniagua gave Enovid with the usual warnings that they might experience side effects. To no one's surprise, such side effects were reported by these women in 23 percent of their early cycles under Enovid medication.

He instructed a second small group, which had been using other contraceptives, to take Enovid as well for a few months, "to see if they were suited to continue using this method." But unknown to these women and to the social workers who interviewed them, they actually received not

Enovid but placebo pills made up of lactose sugar. Although these inert pills were incapable of evoking any true physical effects, such "side effects"—which could only have been psychological—were nonetheless reported for 17 percent of the medication cycles.

Finally, Dr. Paniagua pulled a third rabbit out of his hat. He gave real Enovid to a new group of volunteers, but both he and the social workers carefully avoided any suggestion that they might experience any discomfort at all. Among this group, reactions were reported for only a bit more than 6 percent of the medication cycles.

It thus became clear that while the 10-milligram doses of Enovid which were then being used did indeed evoke some true side effects similar to those noted in early pregnancy, these occurred with far less frequency than had originally been supposed. Between 50 and 60 percent of all the side effects reported by volunteers were either entirely or partially psychological in origin, resulting from the user's apprehension that she would experience them.

In contrast to these unpleasant reactions, the field trials revealed innumerable instances of highly desirable side effects. From their very first cycle of Enovid medication onward, more than 70 percent of all women reported that they felt better than before. After two or three months of using Enovid—when their own experience confirmed the field workers' assurances that the pills were indeed effective as contraceptives—many women lost their chronic fear of a new pregnancy which had soured their sexual relations with their husbands. Instead of making excuses to avoid sexual contacts, they found themselves more responsive to their husbands' advances and increasingly capable of enjoying the intercourse which previously had been spoiled for them by a dread of its consequences.

Beyond these psychological benefits, however, hundreds of the volunteers experienced distinctly physical benefits as well. After two or three cycles of Enovid medication, approximately 50 percent of the women who had previously suffered from difficult and painful menstrual periods reported that they were largely or completely relieved of such pains. Among volunteers who had previously experienced acute premenstrual tension, approximately 50 percent reported relief. Of the volunteers who had suffered from excessive bleeding during menstrual periods prior to using Enovid, some 80 percent experienced a pronounced reduction of menstrual flow after one or more cycles of using the pills as a contraceptive.

When the possibility of controlling fertility by means of a physiologically active ovulation inhibitor was first established, many a hormone researcher feared that after prolonged use of such steroids, many women might find their fertility seriously reduced if they were not indeed rendered entirely sterile. Dr. Rock's Brookline experiments refuted these fears only with respect to short-term use, two or three months, of the 19-nor steroids. The preliminary field trials at San Juan, as we have seen, made it clear that up to nine months of contraception with Enovid did not prevent women from becoming pregnant when they again desired to have children. But the subsequent, full-scale field trials laid this worry to rest, even with respect to women who used Enovid continuously for four full years or more.

Dr. Satterthwaite, for example, followed up the experiences of 256 women who, for one reason or another, had withdrawn from the Humacao study. She found that far from having suffered any impairment of their fertility, all but three of these women had become pregnant; nearly two thirds of them within three months of ceasing to use the oral contraceptive. Sixty-three, in fact, had achieved a second pregnancy at the time of the follow-up study. The over-all pregnancy rate among this group was actually twice as high as that of the Humacao volunteers before they enrolled in the field trials.

An examination of 197 of the babies delivered by these women revealed only three major and two minor congenital defects, an incidence no greater than that among babies born to women in the same age groups in the general Puerto Rican population. "The use of Enovid," Dr. Satterthwaite reported, "led to no increase in complications of pregnancy or of delivery. . . . We have detected no evidence of damage from the prolonged use of the compound."

When field trials were first started in Puerto Rico, some endocrinologists had feared that the prolonged use of a synthetic progestational agent and of estrogen might touch off the growth of cervical, uterine, or breast cancer. Thus, from 1956 onward, women taking part in the tests received thorough periodic physical examinations, including Papanicolaou cytological smear tests for cervical cancer. As the clinical trials were extended to other locations in Puerto Rico, these rigorous testing procedures were applied to every woman participating in the experiments.

These tests not only revealed no rise in the incidence of uterine cancer; they showed that women who used the pill were developing pre-cancerous conditions far less frequently than were non-users of comparable age in Puerto Rico's general population.

On the basis of these early studies the American Cancer Society and the Andre and Bella Meyer Foundation made substantial grants to finance even more intensive examinations of women participating in the Puerto Rican and Haitian field trials, studies which have continued over a period of more than eight years.

As women have joined these new experimental groups they have been assigned, at random, use of either oral contraceptives or of conventional "old style" vaginal jellies, creams, foams, suppositories, or diaphragms. The women in both groups have been repeatedly receiving examinations and tests designed to reveal the presence of breast cancer and of pre-cancerous vaginal conditions.

To date, all the evidence gathered by these intensive studies indicates that oral contraceptives not only do not induce cancer indications; they appear to be protective against both cancer of the cervix and of the breast. For instance, the Papanicolaou vaginal smear test has revealed abnormal, possibly pre-cancerous cells in 3.6 percent of a control group of three thousand non-users of the oral contraceptive. In sharp contrast, such pre-cancerous cells have been found in only 1.6 percent of the 6,000 women in the study who have been using oral contraceptive pills for two years or longer. Thus, up to now, the incidence of suspicious vaginal smears among pill-users has been less than one half as high as in the non-pill-using group.

The incidence of breast cancer among women in the twenty-five to thirty-nine-year-old age group in Puerto Rico is some twenty cases per thousand. But among the six thousand women in the same age group who have been using oral contraceptives as participants in these studies, not a single case of breast cancer has as yet been diagnosed.

Investigators conducting clinical trials of Enovid in the continental United States have also routinely made extensive use of cancer-testing procedures and found no evidence that the pill caused cancer of any kind. Dr. Edward Tyler, for example, reported: "Our fairly extensive pathologic studies thus far do not indicate that these compounds [oral contraceptives] produce malignant changes in the genital tissue, or genital tract rather, of women using them." Writing in the *Journal of the American Medical Association*, Dr. John Rock declared: "If [Enovid's] use bears any relation to malignancy, all signs so far point to its being anti-carcinogenic."

Findings such as these have substantially increased the hope that users of oral contraceptives may concomitantly gain a substantial degree of protection against cervical and breast cancers. Before this important point can be conclusively decided, however, further studies over a period of years will be necessary.

By 1960 the Puerto Rican and Haitian field trials—and the many other series of trials conducted by clinical researchers in the continental United States—had established beyond all doubt Enovid's efficacy as a contraceptive. Its side effects had been revealed and found to affect only a fraction of all users during the first few months and only occasional users in later months. Its safety in continued use over extended periods had been clearly demonstrated. Thus, the question was no longer whether it would be proper to permit physicians to prescribe the pills when contraceptives were indicated. Time and research had turned the question upside down. Both the clinical researchers and the Searle Company now had to ask themselves whether, in good conscience, they could any longer deny Enovid's contraceptive power to the thousands of physicians and the millions of their patients who had heard of the new contraceptive's existence and were clamoring for a chance to use it.

At Skokie, therefore, Drs. Raymond and Winter prepared a detailed New Drug Application for submission to the Federal Food and Drug Administration. Supplementing it, they sent a three-foot-high stack of reports on all the studies made upon laboratory animals and all the tests on human volunteers. Then, for months, the FDA's physicians, pharmacologists, chemists, and other scientists evaluated this wealth of information. At last, in May of 1960, the FDA granted its approval for the marketing of Enovid as a contraceptive, to be used on physicians' prescription. (Enovid had previously been approved, in 1957, for use by physicians in the treatment of threatened abortion and menstrual disorders.) Following the Searle company's cautious recommendation, the FDA set the maximum period of continuous use of Enovid as a contraceptive—for the time being—at two years, even though clinical experience already strongly indicated the compound's safety when used for substantially longer periods.

In July of 1962, after Enovid had been in general use as a contraceptive for more than two years, Dr. Edwin DeCosta, Professor of Obstetrics and Gynecology at the Northwestern University School of Medicine, noted that several of his patients who had been taking birth control pills had developed inflammations of the veins in their legs. Because these inflammations could have involved blood clots, or thromboses, Dr. DeCosta wondered whether they might have been caused, in some way, by the contraceptive compound. He reported his observations in the *Journal of the American Medical Association* and shortly thereafter several other physicians reported similar thrombophlebitic manifestations. A few weeks later the *British Medical Journal* reported four similar cases of leg vein trouble among women taking the pill. One of these patients had died, presumably when a blood clot broke away from the wall of a vein and traveled and blocked a vital artery. Searle officials promptly notified the FDA of these reports.

Many other new drugs have also evoked reports of suspected deleterious effects. In its booklet "Facts for Consumers," the Food and Drug Administration explains how it normally handles this sort of situation:

> Even the most thorough premarketing trials on human beings involve only a small number of patients compared with the number that may take the drug after it gets on the market.
>
> As more and more people use the drug, there is a greater chance that side effects or previously undiscovered disadvantages will show up.
>
> It would be impossible to require enough animal and clinical testing to detect an incidence of one drug-induced case of serious adverse reaction per 100,000 patients getting the drug. And yet any such incidence would be a matter of serious concern.
>
> It is therefore necessary to keep a watch over new drugs after they go on the market.
>
> The 1962 amendments require manufacturers to report to FDA any information on adverse effects or other new clinical experience with new drugs and antibiotics after they are marketed.
>
> If a drug is found to present an imminent hazard to health, any previous approval can be suspended immediately.

While the FDA could thus have immediately suspended its approval of the marketing of Enovid and forbidden further sale, it decided that the suspicions which had been raised did not warrant any action so drastic, because the clots might very well have occurred even if the women involved had not been taking Enovid. Thus it asked the Searle Company to send a so-called "Dear Doctor" letter to all practicing physicians to alert them to the situation. Searle's officials went further than that. Within four hectic days they produced more than three hundred thousand letters which were mailed not only to all actively practicing U.S. doctors but to those not in active practice, and to every doctor of osteopathy, every hospital, and every pharmacist in both the United States and Canada.

At the same time, both the Searle Company and the FDA initiated studies designed to find the answer to the crucial question of whether or not there was any *causal* relationship between the long-term cyclic use of Enovid and the occurrence of thrombophlebitis. This condition was known to occur in women taking no drugs at all. Almost every doctor has observed some such cases in the course of his practice. But, strangely enough, no one had ever determined how frequently it occurs and under what circumstances. Even the Division of Vital Statistics of the U.S. Public Health Service found it had no adequate data on the incidence of thrombophlebitis or the number of deaths resulting from it. Thus, the first necessity was to find some way of filling in this surprising blank area in medical statistics.

Dr. Robert Burket of the Department of Obstetrics of the Cincinnati General Hospital, for example, undertook the monumental task of combing through the records of all twelve hospitals of the Greater Cincinnati area in order to determine the normal incidence of thrombophlebitis in this large and typical American community. To do so, he had to analyze the records of nearly sixty thousand female patients of childbearing age—from fifteen through forty-four—admitted during 1959. And he found that 102 cases involving spontaneous thrombophlebitis or pulmonary embolism had occurred during that year, although not one of these women had been using oral contraceptive pills.

Dr. J. D. Ramsay, Director of the Research and Statistics Branch of the Department of Public Health of the Canadian Province of Saskatchewan, made a similar study of 135,000 women of childbearing age who were enrolled in the state-supported medical program. His figures revealed that in 1957 there had been 112 cases of thrombophlebitis among non-pregnant women, none of whom—of course—had taken any birth control pills.

In September of 1962 a "grand jury" of twenty-nine distinguished epidemiologists, blood specialists, gynecologists, and statisticians met at the headquarters of the American Medical Association under the chairmanship of Professor Michael E. DeBakey, Professor of Surgery at the Baylor University School of Medicine, for a day-long discussion and evaluation of all available evidence relating to the occurrence of thrombophlebitis both in pill-users and in the general public. At the end of their meeting, twenty-eight of the twenty-nine experts declared that they found no evidence that the pills caused thrombophlebitis. The one remaining member of the panel, Dr. Stanford Wessler of the Harvard Medical School, did not vote against his colleagues. He abstained from voting because he felt that there was not yet enough evidence to support a decision either way.

A few months later a separate, independent investigation was arranged by the American Medical Association. The A.M.A. found "absolutely no evidence that use of the oral contraceptive caused the reported cases of thrombophlebitis."

Then, in January of 1963, the Food and Drug Administration set up an *ad hoc* committee of nine distinguished experts under the chairmanship of Dr. Irving S. Wright, Clinical Professor of Medicine of the Cornell University Medical College, to evaluate any possible etiological relation of Enovid with thromboembolic conditions.* Over a period of eight months the Wright Committee analyzed mountains of data accumulated by its members, by the FDA, by Searle's consultants, and by numerous other investigators. Its final report, submitted in September, 1963, concluded: "On the basis of available data, no significant increase in the risk of thromboembolic death from the use of Enovid . . . has been demonstrated."

Shortly after the Wright Committee reached this conclusion the Food and Drug Administration extended the permissible period for the continuous use of Enovid as a contraceptive from two years to four. Contraindications were few. Physicians are cautioned to rule out the possibility of the presence of cancer of the genital tract or of the breasts before instituting Enovid therapy. They are advised against prescribing Enovid for patients who have previously experienced thrombophlebitis or pulmonary embolism unless the reason for such use is, in the doctor's judgment, overwhelming. Similarly, the drug is not to be prescribed for women with suspected or overt liver diseases. And doctors are also cautioned to carefully control the use of Enovid—and to discontinue its use when necessary—in diabetics and in patients susceptible to thyroid dysfunctions.

Since 1960 the field trials of Enovid have been continued and expanded so that many women, by now, have used the

* The other committee members were Dr. Leonard M. Schuman, Professor of Public Health of the University of Minnesota; Dr. Willard M. Allen, Chief of the Division of Gynecology and Obstetrics of the Washington University School of Medicine; Dr. Roy Hertz, Chief of Endocrinology Branch of the National Cancer Institute; Dr. Benjamin Alexander, Associate Professor of Medicine of Harvard University; Dr. George Penick of the University of North Carolina School of Medicine; Dr. William Crosby of the Institute of Research of Walter Reed Army Medical Center; Dr. Carroll Lattimore Spurling, Associate Professor of Medicine of the University of Maryland Medical School; and Dr. John A. Spittell, Jr., Clinical Pathologist of the Mayo Clinic.

drug as a contraceptive for as long as eight years without any ill effect. But throughout the United States an infinitely larger, unofficial "field test" has been conducted over the last five years by tens of thousands of physicians who have written more than ten million Enovid prescriptions for their patients. Throughout the rest of the world, many additional millions have also found Enovid 100 percent effective in protecting against unwanted pregnancy, when taken as directed.

Thus, Dr. Stone's old dream of an ideal contraceptive—and Dr. Pincus' interpretation of it as a physiological oral contraceptive—have both come true. Today, this product of more than fifteen years of continuous research and testing, which so many worked so long to perfect, is rapidly effecting a quiet revolution in the marital happiness of millions of couples, in the health and prosperity of their families, and in all the world's views regarding contraception and the control of its explosively growing population.

9
•

BIRTH CONTROL IN
REVERSE

•

Throughout all human history, millions upon millions of marriages have been blighted by barrenness. Whether or not they have wanted children at first, almost all couples decide sooner or later, "Now is the time." For most, this decision is almost enough. But too many others watch the months turn to years in an increasing agony of frustration and mutual suspicion. For many a couple the bitterness of fruitless yearning ends only in the divorce courts—if, for the childless, it may be said ever to end at all.

Involuntary childlessness is, in fact, far more common than most people suppose. Despite the baby-boom since World War II, 17 percent of all marriages in this country have produced no children; 5 per cent more are instances of so-called one-child sterility, women who have been unable to achieve a second pregnancy or to carry it to term. At the present time there are, in the United States alone, at least three million couples striving and hoping for the parenthood they haven't yet managed to achieve.

From time immemorial such couples have resorted to all sorts of magic and incantations in the hope of gaining relief from the curse of infertility. Until about fifty years ago, in fact, medicine had nothing more to offer them than the usually futile prescription: keep trying. But as physiologists and physicians began to explore the intricate mechanisms of the human reproductive organs, it gradually became apparent to them that barrenness was not a single "something"; that it was rather the result of one or more of a vast number of specific malformations or malfunctionings of the reproductive organs. And with this realization came the first glimmer of hope that medical science might play a truly effective role in the overcoming of infertility.

In the past men have almost always imposed the shame and the blame of a childless marriage upon their wives, refusing—with typical male arrogance—even to contemplate the possibility that the fault might lie partly or wholly with them. In many countries, even today, a husband may cast off and divorce a wife simply because she has failed to give him children. But the earliest scientific studies of the male organs and of the seed they produce revealed that innumerable cases of barrenness arose solely or largely because of the husband's infertility. Today fertility researchers ascribe fully one third of all cases of barrenness to male deficiencies.

A husband may lack nothing in sexual prowess. But, because of disease or endocrine disturbance, his semenal emissions may contain no sperm capable of fertilizing his wife's perfectly normal, waiting ovum. This *azoospermia*, early researchers discovered, might result from such infections as mumps which is sometimes complicated by an inflammation of the testicles which destroys their sperm-forming ability. In other instances sperm production may proceed normally but obstructions in the semenal ducts may block the passage of the male sex cells into the husband's semenal ejaculate. More frequently the male's semen may be so deficient in the number of its normal sperm cells as to reduce the chance of fertilization almost to zero.

The normally fertile male, for example, ejaculates approximately four hundred million sperm cells in a single semenal emission. Nature seems to provide this vast number of cells as a sort of insurance that at least one will be able to make its way to the female ovum and achieve a fertilizing penetration of that egg cell. But in a surprisingly large number of men all sorts of causes, long-term or temporary, may reduce the quantity of the sperm and thus greatly decrease the chance of successful fertilization. When the number of sperm cells falls below a hundred million per emission, the male's hope of fatherhood vanishes almost entirely.

In still other cases a husband's semenal emission may contain a seemingly adequate number of sperm cells but a very high proportion of these may lack the motility essential for their "swim" to the egg cell. For the sperm is the only human cell that must move entirely under its own power. If properly formed it possesses a vigorously wiggling tail which propels it forward just as if it were a minuscule trout making its way upstream against a rushing current.

From its point of deposit in the vagina it must swim only nine or ten inches—through the cervix and the Fallopian tubes—to find and fertilize the ovum. But all during this trip its progress is being fought by millions of tiny hair-like cells, which waft a current *down* the Fallopian tubes.

Nine or ten inches may not sound like a long distance to travel. To a microscopically tiny sperm, however, this is the equivalent of what a trout would have to accomplish in making its way up 150 miles of boiling rapids. To put the sturdy trout to further shame, the sperm scorns to take the easy path straight up the middle. It multiplies the distance of its non-stop swim by ambling from bank to bank a few dozen thousand times. Thus the sperm that finally makes the grade must be a mighty motile sperm indeed. And if any large proportion of the male's sperm cells are lacking in motility, the odds against fertilization rise disastrously.

Often the semen of the male partner in an infertile marriage may be found to be deficient in both the number and motility of its sperm cells. In the hope of overcoming such deficiencies many physicians have tried to build up the general health of infertile males with dietary supplements and vitamin prescriptions.

Other researchers noted that childless couples often attempt to boost the odds in favor of conception by increasing the frequency of their sexual intercourse. In doing so, however, they sometimes defeat the very end they seek, by depleting the husband's supply of available mature sperm cells. Since the testes can replenish their sperm cell reserve only over a period of several days, too frequent sexual activity may thus prevent a man from providing a sufficiently rich semenal fluid to offer any hope of fertilization. Thus, quite logically, physicians have advised infertile couples to deliberately reduce the frequency of sexual activity and to time their intercourse for those days immediately after ovulation is estimated to have occurred.

When testosterone, the male sex hormone, was first isolated it was believed that injections of this steroid might substantially increase a man's production of healthy, motile sperm cells. This hope, however, proved vain. It was found, in fact, that large doses of testosterone actually inhibited sperm production.

Out of this seeming defeat, however, observant clinicians were able to wrest at least a partial victory. In 1950 Dr. Carl George Heller and his co-workers at the University of Oregon Medical School noted that a withdrawal of testosterone administration was followed, in some instances, by a rebound phenomenon. An originally low sperm count, further depressed by testosterone doses, not only returned to its earlier level when testosterone was withdrawn; it actually rose substantially above that level. In a significant number of cases of men who had been seemingly futilely treated with testosterone, the rebound reaction was followed by successful impregnation of their wives.

While physicians have slowly been able to improve their success rate in the relief of male infertility, they have scored much more spectacular progress in the treatment of infertile women. Since the female reproductive organs are far more complicated than those of the male, a woman's fertility may be susceptible to impairment in many more ways. As far back as the 1930s Dr. S. R. Meaker was able to list 320 causes of infertility in women; and researchers have discovered many more since then.

One of the most common of such causes is a blocking of the Fallopian tubes which may result from a childhood disease, a more recent infection, or even from a previous pregnancy. Thus one of the physician's first steps in examining a woman who has been unable to become pregnant is to test the patency or openness of these tiny passages, using a method invented more than four decades ago by one of the outstanding pioneers of fertility research, Dr. I. C. Rubin, Professor of Gynecology at the New York University College of Medicine.

Under aseptic conditions, the physician pumps a small quantity of carbon dioxide gas into his patient's womb. If the tubes are open, the gas will pass through them into the pelvic cavity and the patient will feel, for a moment, a sharp pain in her shoulder. The physician can also tell whether the gas is passing through the tubes by watching the pressure-indicating dial on his patency-testing device. If the tubes are blocked, the indicator will remain motionless; if they are open, the needle will move slowly backward. (Some physicians prefer to employ iodized oil for patency tests. While the details of this method differ somewhat from that of the carbon dioxide technique, both rely upon essentially the same principle.)

In some instances in which the Fallopian tubes are blocked by scar tissue or adhesions as a result of old inflammations, a delicate surgical operation is necessary to open them. Before resorting to such surgery, however, physicians usually repeat the tubal test a number of times, because the mere performance of this gentle pressure-inducing procedure is often sufficient to open the hair-thin

passages. Some years ago, in a study of fifty thousand repeated tubal insufflations, Dr. Rubin found that almost
seven thousand of these were followed by pregnancy,
sometimes within a month or two. More recently Dr. E. C.
Hamblen, Professor of Endocrinology at the Duke University School of Medicine, attributed 54 percent of the
pregnancies which occurred to the childless couples he and
his associates treated to the establishment of tubal patency
by the iodized-oil method.

By reopening blocked Fallopian tubes—or correcting
other anatomical barriers to the meeting of sperm and
ovum—physicians have been able to relieve from 8 to 10
percent of all cases of female sterility that come before
them for treatment. In a far, far larger proportion of instances, however, infertility is the result of endocrine deficiencies or imbalances rather than of physical barriers to
fertilization. Thus, ever since the first female sex hormones
became available, clinical researchers have attempted to use
them to restore to the reproductive organs a normal pattern of functioning.

As we have seen in Chapter 7, it was with precisely
such a purpose that Dr. John Rock began his pseudopregnancy experiments upon infertile patients in the early
1950s. His convincing demonstration that such pseudopregnancies could be brought about by the oral administration of Enovid—and that an unexpectedly high proportion
of previously sterile women could achieve true pregnancies
after several months of Enovid-induced pseudopregnancies
—inevitably led many other gynecologists to explore the
usefulness of this new synthetic steroid compound for the relief of a number of types of endocrine-imbalance infertility.
One obvious point of attack was in the treatment of

so-called secondary amenorrhea, the fairly common condition in which young women cease to menstruate because their ovaries fail to mature and release a fertilizable egg cell each month. Among the first such experimenters was Dr. Maxwell Roland of the Albert Einstein College of Medicine in New York who, in 1955 and 1956, conducted a pilot study on nineteen patients who had been infertile for from two to ten years. He used essentially the same pattern of cyclic therapy with Enovid that Dr. Rock had utilized in his Brookline experiments. But, unlike Dr. Rock, he did not restrict his volunteers to women who were demonstrably ovulating. Instead he deliberately included among his patients ten women who had been shown, through a series of tests, to be non-ovulators.

Just as in Rock's earlier experiments, Dr. Roland's withdrawal of Enovid after twenty days of therapy was almost always followed by menstrual bleeding. When therapy was ended after several Enovid-induced cycles the women continued to experience a normal menstrual pattern. And within two or three months after the end of Enovid therapy three of Dr. Roland's nineteen patients, including one who had not previously been ovulating, became pregnant. Thus the presumption was at least tentatively established that cyclic pseudopregnancies could not only restore menstruation, but—as was true in at least one instance—could apparently restore ovulation as well.

Continuing his research, Dr. Roland extended his experiments to thirty-nine non-ovulating volunteers. Among these, after from two to three months of cyclic therapy with Enovid, a substantial number began to ovulate. And this time three of these women—previously infertile because their ovaries were failing to release an egg cell—achieved pregnancy.

That this was no mere coincidental happenstance, unrelated to cyclic therapy with the new drug, was demonstrated when such other researchers as Drs. Harry
Kupperman and Jeanne A. Epstein, of the New York
University School of Medicine, and Dr. Jay Gold, of Chicago's Michael Reese Hospital, reported the achievement
of similar results among their own formerly non-menstru-
ating, non-ovulating patients.

One of the strangest, yet most common, causes of infertility is a painful condition known as endometriosis.
Normally the outer layers of the endometrium, or lining
of the uterus, are shed during every woman's menstrual
periods and carried away through the vagina with her
menstrual blood flow. But in some women, for reasons
physiologists do not yet fully understand, bits of endometrial tissue may migrate *upward* through the Fallopian
tubes and into the abdominal cavity. There they may implant themselves upon the outer surfaces of the ovaries, the
bladder, the colon, or the ligaments that support the uterus.

In these new locations these misplaced groups of cells
continue to function as endometrial tissue. It is not known
for certain whether they grow and spread to cover larger
areas of the organs to which they attach themselves, or
whether a gradual increase of endometriosis results from
repeated menstrual backflows. Possibly both of these processes occur. But, in any event, the same cyclic drop-off
in the production of estrogen and progesterone which
touches off normal endometrial shedding in the uterus also
causes these misplaced endometrial tissues to undergo mini-
ature menstruations every month.

The results are painful and even crippling. An endometrial growth upon the ureter, which carries urine from the

kidney to the bladder, may actually clamp down upon and obstruct this delicate tube. If the bladder's outer surface is involved, the victim of endometriosis may experience a constant discomfort and urge to urinate. If endometrial tissues attach themselves to the sigmoid colon, they may cause dangerous bowel obstructions. These transported cells may form large blood-filled cysts upon the ovary which occasionally rupture, with serious consequences. In many women endometrial proliferation in the pelvic area can make sexual intercourse unbearably painful. Worst of all, for the woman who wants a child, the growth of these tissues upon the ovaries and the ends of the Fallopian tubes can make the passage of ova into the tubes impossible and thus produce total infertility.

Physicians have no direct means of measuring the incidence of endometriosis among the female population at large, since many, who may actually be victims of this abnormal tissue migration, accept its painful symptoms as natural "women's troubles" and never report them to their family doctors. Thus the condition is often diagnosed only when it has reached an advanced stage. But gynecologists specializing in the treatment of infertility do have a very clear idea of how great a role it plays in preventing conception. At the Brookline Free Hospital for Women, for example, so-called infertility laparotomies—operations performed in the course of fertility treatment—reveal endometriosis in fully one third of all cases. In other words, one out of every three women whose primary complaint is infertility have been found to suffer, to a greater or lesser extent, from this crippling disease.

Until a few years ago physicians had only one method of treating endometriosis, a drastic one which they used most reluctantly: abdominal surgery to remove the uterus and both ovaries. Since this procedure ended all menstruation, it put an end to the monthly intra-abdominal bleeding of the misplaced, implanted endometrial growths. But far from relieving infertility, such surgical castration simply made it final and permanently irreversible.

As a more conservative alternative a number of gynecologists attempted to suppress the disease by the administration of such synthetic male hormones as methyltestosterone. When they used small doses they achieved little or none of the desired effect. Larger doses suppressed ovulation and thus avoided intra-abdominal "menstrual" bleeding. But this experimental treatment often induced virilizing side effects: women developed acne, hoarseness, edema, facial hair growths, enlargement of the clitoris, and sometimes a form of jaundice.

Thus, until 1955, physicians faced a Hobson's choice between the undesirable alternatives of a surgical castration that ended all hope of childbearing and a type of hormone therapy which tended to inflict upon women a brand-new set of utterly repugnant symptoms without assuring the elimination of their infertility.

The man who radically altered this sorry situation was Dr. Robert W. Kistner, Assistant Professor of Obstetrics and Gynecology at the Harvard Medical School and Associate Surgeon at the Free Hospital for Women. One of his patients, a nurse who had long suffered from endometriosis of both ovaries, was nonetheless lucky enough to become pregnant. Fortunately for the advancement of medicine she was unlucky enough to require delivery by Caesarian section. And when Dr. Kistner performed this operation he noted that her endometriotic growths had almost entirely regressed. Microscopic examination of the involved areas on the ovaries showed that the endometrial cells had undergone a process of necrosis; they had died away, become liquefied and absorbed during the nine months in which pregnancy itself had inhibited ovulation and prevented menstruation.

As a colleague and close friend of Dr. John Rock, Bob Kistner had followed with deep interest the Rock-Pincus-Garcia pseudopregnancy experiments. Faced with the fact that a *real* pregnancy had apparently brought about the "cure" of a severe case of endometriosis, he felt compelled to investigate whether the same effect could be obtained by means of a prolonged pseudopregnancy induced by a progestin-estrogen combination such as Enovid.

Early in 1956 Dr. Kistner began gathering together a group of endometriosis victims, from among his own private patients and from the out-patient department of the Free Hospital for Women. To each he carefully described the experiments that Dr. Rock and his associates had already conducted in seeking the relief of infertility by cyclic therapy with Enovid. Then he explained to these women why cyclic treatments followed by menstruation were most unlikely to prove of any benefit in relieving their troubles. Instead he warned them that his plan of treatment would require the continuous administration of the progestin-estrogen medication for from six to nine months and possibly longer. All were also warned that they might experience uncomfortable side effects. And all were explicitly told that in an experiment of this sort, they could be given no assurances of any improvement of their condition, much less a cure.

Despite all of these warnings, a dozen women promptly enrolled in a pilot experimental group. For the first two weeks of treatment each woman swallowed 2.5 or 5 milligrams daily, a deliberately small dose designed to minimize such early side effects as nausea. As each patient became accustomed to the drug her daily dosage was stepped up over two-week intervals to 10 milligrams, then 15, and finally to 20 milligrams a day for the remainder of her treatment period. And each volunteer periodically returned to the Free Hospital for a thorough examination, including, in many cases, a direct viewing of the condition of her endometriotic tissues by means of a culdoscope.

This ingenious instrument utilizes a sharply pointed, metallic tube which can painlessly pierce a thin area in the wall of the abdominal cavity. Once inserted, a system of lenses, mirrors, and bright lights inside the tube permits the physician to examine visually the surfaces of the reproductive organs, the ureter, the bladder, and the colon. When this examination is completed, the tube is withdrawn and its point of entry closes naturally without bleeding.

By the second or third month of treatment the patients in this pilot study were enthusiastically reporting substantial relief of pain and other subjective improvements. Culdoscopic observations also provided objective confirmation of such improvement as the areas of endometriotic tissues began to shrink and be reabsorbed.

Though it was far too early to draw any firm conclusions from these first favorable indications, other women suffering from endometriosis began to clamor for admission to the experimental project. Within the next few months a number of private patients of Drs. Paul A. Younge, Herbert W. Horne, and Charles Easterday—and additional volunteers from the Free Hospital's out-patient department—increased the experimental group to fifty-eight. Over the next two years, as eleven Boston gynecologists joined what had now become a large cooperative project, the number of volunteers under this new therapy gradually grew to over two hundred.

As in any such experiment a few patients dropped the treatment, either because they found side effects unpleasant or for such non-medical reasons such as a change of residence to a distant area. But of the vast majority who faithfully followed Dr. Kistner's program for six months or longer, some 83 percent experienced increasing subjective and objective improvements in their condition. When their treatment was stopped these patients promptly resumed a normal pattern of ovulation and menstruation. And, under continued observation, the remissions achieved by prolonged pseudopregnancy treatments with Enovid were maintained month after month, for up to four years or longer.

Most important of all, an astounding 47 percent of the patients who tried to conceive a child after their treatment, became pregnant—frequently during their second or third post-therapy ovulation.

These unexpectedly favorable results were soon confirmed by many other clinical experimenters. For example, in a series of ninety-two patients treated by Cmdr. Thomas B. Lebherz and Lt. Clark D. Fobes at the Naval Medical Center in Bethesda, Maryland, and at the Washington Navy Dispensary, Enovid-induced pseudopregnancies "produced subjective and objective relief both during and after therapy in 75 to 80 percent of the cases."

At the Walter Reed Hospital, Col. H. L. Riva, Capt. D. M. Kawasaki, and Capt. A. J. Messenger treated 132 patients with Enovid for an average of about six months. "Complete regression," they reported in the *Journal of Obstetrics and Gynecology*, "was objectively reported in

69 percent; patients showing either no residual evidence of endometriosis or scarred inactive areas at sites of previous involvement. Fourteen additional patients (11%) showed objective improvement although regression was incomplete. Another eight (6%) were clinically improved following their therapy."

In this study fourteen patients—who had not notably improved during their first six months of treatment—were continued on Enovid for an additional three to nine months and then re-evaluated. In four instances Dr. Riva and his associates found that the extended course of treatment had produced a complete regression of endometriosis; in two more patients marked improvement was observed. And once again a substantial portion of those patients who sought conception after their pseudopregnancies found their previous infertility relieved and were able to become pregnant within a few months after the cessation of Enovid therapy.

Similar results have been reported by Dr. Robert B. Greenblatt, Professor of Endocrinology of the Medical College of Georgia; Dr. C. Herman Weinberg, senior Gynecologist of the Touro Infirmary of New Orleans; Drs. William C. Andrews, Mason C. Andrews, and A. F. Strauss of the Norfolk General Hospital; Dr. Bruce F. P. Williams of the Duluth Clinic, and a number of other investigators. In the course of these studies it has been found that endometriosis may successfully be treated by using smaller doses of Enovid than were originally thought necessary. As this is written, reports of clinical investigations, covering several thousand women with endometriosis treated by pseudopregnancy, have been published in American medical journals; a number of similar studies have appeared in journals in Britain, Canada, Australia, and other countries. To these thousands of cases, observed under close clinical control, must be added many others who have experienced remissions of endometriosis—and often achieved pregnancies previously denied them—under treatment as the private or clinic patients of physicians who now accept pseudopregnancy as a well-established form of therapy and thus feel no need for publishing special reports.

Still another major cause of infertility is a condition for which physicians use such names as *inadequate endometrium*, or *defective luteal phase*, or *endocrine sterility*, or *poor corpus luteum function*, or *deficient secretion phase*, or *secretory hypoplasia of the endometrium*. All of these terms are merely slightly different ways of describing the same complex phenomenom. In everyday English, they come down to saying, "Some women are able to achieve pregnancy—but only for a few hours or a few days." Tragically, their fertilized ovum fails to implant itself in the wall of the uterus and thus, in effect, they suffer an abortion without missing a menstrual period and without ever knowing that they have been, at least momentarily, pregnant.

Until recently, while physicians knew that many women were unable to maintain an early pregnancy because of luteal deficiency, they had no clear picture of how often this condition lay behind a couple's sterility. But in 1955 Dr. John S. Gillam reported, in the *Journal of Fertility and Sterility*, on a study he had made of 123 infertile patients. He found that fifty-seven of these, over 46 percent of the entire group, were victims of deficient luteal secretion. In a more recent study Drs. B. A. Foss, Herbert W. Horne, and Arthur Tremaine Hertig were able to diagnose luteal

deficiency in an even higher proportion of infertile patients. In not all of these, of course, is this deficiency the
sole cause of infertility. But as a result of these studies it is
now definitely known that between 40 and 50 percent of
all infertile women have their hopes of pregnancy frustrated by this single type of endocrine malfunction.

In a normal woman's monthly rhythm, estrogen, produced in the ovaries, dominates the first half of her cycle.
Under its influence one of the hundreds of follicles in her
ovaries grows and within it an egg cell advances toward
maturity. In this same period the lining of her uterus,
which had shed most of its endometrial cells during menstruation, begins to build a new, gradually thickening endometrial tissue. Then, usually about the fourteenth day of
her cycle, the follicle ruptures and releases the mature
ovum, which passes into the Fallopian tubes. If intercourse
takes place within the next day or two, fertilization is
likely. And if this occurs the now fertilized egg moves
onward into the uterus where, if all goes well, it attaches
itself to the endometrium and begins its nine months of
fetal maturation.

But the follicle, once it has ruptured and released its egg,
has by no means completed the tasks nature has provided
for it. Within that small sac there is a yellowish mass of
material, called the corpus luteum, which secretes the female hormone progesterone. Under progesterone's influence the endometrium undergoes a new stage of growth,
the stage essential for its successful reception and nourish-
ment of the fertilized egg for the ensuing first months of
pregnancy.

Unfortunately, the secretion of corpus luteum is deficient
in many women. And because of this poor corpus luteum
function, or defective luteal phase, the endometrium is in-

adequately prepared to foster and maintain the nesting and early growth of the fertilized egg. Instead, the ordinary cycle continues as if fertilization had never occurred. The endometrial tissue begins to disintegrate and is shed in menstruation. And along with it goes the fertilized egg and a wasted, incipient pregnancy.

As far back as the start of the twentieth century, hormone researchers began to understand the stages of the normal reproductive cycle and, particularly, the vital function of the corpus luteum. By 1929 Drs. Willard M. Allen and George W. Corner prepared extracts of corpus luteum which endocrinologists began to use, tentatively and experimentally, in the hope of supplementing the deficient corpus luteum supply of women unable to maintain a pregnancy through its first few days. By 1934 the active hormone of corpus luteum had been isolated, synthesized, and named progesterone—descriptive of its function of supporting gestation or fetal growth. Physicians thus obtained a better, but by no means perfect, means of preventing the infertilities arising from an inadequate endometrium due to a deficiency of natural hormone secretion.

When the orally active 19-nor steroid progestins became available, however, a great new opportunity opened up for the control of this type of infertility. One of the first to realize this possibility and to explore it thoroughly was Dr. Edward W. Tyler of Los Angeles. In 1955, in his private practice and at the Los Angeles Planned Parenthood Center, he began what has since become one of the longest and most intensive studies involving the use of Enovid in the relief of infertility. Using a battery of tests, he and his associates were able to single out, from among all of their infertile patients, those women who evidenced poor corpus luteum function. To such patients they began to give small daily doses of 19-nor progestin-estrogen preparations as soon as a slight rise in body temperature indicated the occurrence of ovulation. If menstruation followed—that is, if the patient's ovum had not been fertilized—therapy was halted until a new cycle offered a new opportunity for treatment. If, on the other hand, pregnancy tests proved positive, the supplemental administration of the new steroids was continued throughout the first five months of gestation.

By 1957 Dr. Tyler and his colleague, Dr. H. J. Olsen, were able to report on the treatment of sixty-four such patients with Enovid for one or more cycles. Two became pregnant in the very first cycle, three more in the second cycle, and seven others after from three to six cycles of supplemental hormone therapy. "The new steroids," Drs. Tyler and Olsen cautiously reported, "definitely do offer us a better chance of improving fertility in certain patients and of helping them to achieve a pregnancy that might otherwise not occur."

In a 1961 report, after much more extensive experience had supported his earlier judgment, Dr. Tyler declared, "In instances where luteal phase defects are suspected, progestational therapy should be administered during the post-ovulatory phase of the cycle to supplement intrinsic hormone production."

Numerous other clinicians, utilizing patterns of therapy similar to those developed by Dr. Tyler, have reported Enovid to be one of their most effective means of dealing with this type of infertility.

10

•

_____

SAVING THE UNBORN

_____

•

For nearly eight weeks—ever since the laboratory test reports had proved that she was actually pregnant at last—she had thought of herself as the happiest woman on earth. Each morning she awoke with a song in her heart. Throughout each day her hours were filled with gay, anticipatory pictures of her own bright, beautiful baby learning to toddle, starting to talk, calling her "Mother." And every night similar visions of joyous motherhood filled her dreams.

So it was—until the fateful midnight when she was awakened by sharp abdominal cramps and realized in terror that she was about to lose her baby through miscarriage.

• • •

Such spontaneous abortions are no rarity. "Every day," declares Dr. Edith L. Potter, Professor of Pathology in the Obstetric-Gynecologic Department of the University of Chicago, "some twenty-five hundred American women, pregnant for less than six months, suffer miscarriages. Indeed, death before birth is the commonest death of all . . . a tragic wastage of nearly a million babies' lives each year."

For generations the twin questions—Why do miscarriages occur? What should be done to prevent them?—have evoked innumerable, and often bitter, controversies among obstetricians and gynecologists. Many physicians, in fact, looked upon spontaneous abortions as blessings in disguise. As recently as 1940, for example, Dr. Nicholson J. Eastman, Professor of Obstetrics and Obstetrician in Chief at The Johns Hopkins Hospital, declared, "Far from being tragedies, most miscarriages are nature's beneficent way of extinguishing an embryo which is imperfect. This is particularly true of very early miscarriages. Indeed, careful microscopic study of the material passed shows that in 80 percent of these some defect is present in the embryo which is incompatible with life or would result in a grossly deformed child. . . . Miscarriages of this sort are obviously unpreventable and, although bitterly disappointing to the parents, serve in the long run a useful purpose."

Other equally distinguished gynecologists, however, have long and strenuously challenged this theory. They have pointed out that many infants, whose mothers were never threatened by abortion, are nonetheless born with major malformations, while many thousands of other babies, who have survived a threatened miscarriage, have proved to be perfectly normal at birth. "Having carefully examined more than fifteen hundred embryos from miscarriages," Dr. Potter says, "I am quite sure that miscarriages are rarely if ever due to 'bad genes.' Almost all can be attributed to factors which are not inheritable."

Still another widely held theory regarded pregnancy as indeed a "delicate condition" and miscarriages as "accidents" precipitated by excessive activity, overfatigue, or even emotional shock. Thus, many doctors emphatically warned their pregnant patients not to indulge in any strenuous exercises, to give up even the mildest of athletic games, to avoid lifting weights and climbing stairs, to forego jolting auto and train trips, and even never to use a treadle sewing machine.

Many other physicians, however, viewed such prescribed invalidism as not only useless but possibly even dangerous to the health of both mother and child. Enforced inactivity, they argued, might cause muscular atrophy that would make labor a much more prolonged and painful experience than if a woman pursued a normal, moderate pattern of life throughout her pregnancy.

Strongly supporting this latter contention was a study, made some years ago, of the pregnant wives of more than four hundred men stationed at the Robins Air Force Base in Georgia. "During their pregnancies," reports Dr. Potter, "these women had traveled an average of two thousand miles each, by car, bus, train, or plane. Some had crossed the continent in jouncing trucks; some had driven all the way to Alaska and back. Five had been in serious smash-ups; one had actually been catapulted out of her car. Twenty had been extricated from houses demolished by a tornado. Yet the miscarriage rate among these much-buffeted women was no higher than would be expected among women who spent their entire pregnancies placidly sewing little garments in their own homes."

A generation ago almost all pregnant women who bled even slightly—doctors describe such bleeding as "staining" —were advised to take to their beds for fear that any avoidable movement might lead to a miscarriage. But a few years ago Dr. Edward C. Mann, Director of the New York Hospital Recurrent Miscarriage Clinic, wondered whether such prolonged inactivity actually prevented any miscarriages, even among the high-risk group of women who had already experienced one or more spontaneous abortions. To put his doubts to the test, he conducted a controlled experiment. For half of his clinic patients who stained he prescribed the old bed-rest regime; but the remainder were advised to pursue their normal household tasks and merely to avoid overexertion. Months later, when he checked his extensive records, he found that the miscarriage rate was no higher among the women who remained active than among those who took to their beds and stayed there.

Another study, of 1,797 women with symptoms of threatened abortion, confirmed Dr. Mann's observations. The 464 women permitted to resume their household activities after their cramps and staining had subsided did just about as well as the 1,333 confined to their beds. Neither of these studies, of course, indicates that any pregnant woman should blithely ignore even mild staining or fail to inform her doctor promptly of such incidents. What they do indicate to most obstetricians is that bed rest, of itself, is not the cure-all it was once thought to be.

All of these controversies merely reflected the sorry fact that until recent decades, science knew almost nothing about the causes of most miscarriages. As a result physicians had no way of knowing whether any particular woman was likely to sail through a pregnancy in perfect, blooming health or whether "bad luck" would doom her baby to death before birth. Experience had taught doctors that if a woman had already undergone one or more miscarriages, the odds against her next pregnancy running to full term rose enormously. But even for so-called *repeated* or *habitual aborters*—two- and three-time losers—science could offer no clear-cut preventive treatment but only a number of general precautions, time-honored but frequently ineffective. As Dr. Raphael Kurzrok, one of the leading gynecologists of his day, said in 1937, "The reason for our lack of success with our best therapy is relatively simple. We do not as yet understand the physiology of human reproduction."

Even as Dr. Kurzrok wrote these words, however, endocrine researchers were already rapidly accumulating the knowledge that was destined to end the mystery of *why* most miscarriages happen and to lead to new and effective methods of preventing spontaneous abortions.

That progesterone, produced by the corpus luteum, played a major role in preparing the uterus for pregnancy and in guarding the embryo during its first few weeks of growth had been thoroughly demonstrated by the classic experiments of George Corner and his student Willard Allen. But the corpus luteum was known to be only a temporary, short-lived endocrine gland. It began releasing progesterone only when an ovum "hatched" from its sac on the surface of the ovary. If the egg was not fertilized, the corpus luteum withered away within about two weeks and the bleeding phase of the menstrual cycle began. But surgeons had discovered, in the course of emergency abdominal operations upon pregnant women, that when fertilization *did* occur, the corpus luteum remained healthy, yellow, and unshrunken for approximately ten weeks. Operations *after* the first trimester of pregnancy, however, had revealed only withered corpus luteum scar tissue; the gland itself had fulfilled its hormone-producing function and then atrophied.

But why did this happen in the midst of a pregnancy? Could it be that the embryo, at the very time it was growing most rapidly, suddenly ceased to need progesterone to protect its growth? Or might there not rather be some other gland that took over the corpus luteum's function just as that temporary tissue withered away? And if so, what gland would it be?

One possibility was the placenta, the bag-like structure which develops as a protective wall around the embryo. Physiologists had long recognized that one of its major functions is that of an "exchange organ." The mother's bloodstream continually feeds into it nutrients and oxygen which filter through innumerable tiny membranes into the separate fetal blood vessels and thus reach the independent bloodstream of the growing embryo. Fetal waste products are transferred, in the opposite direction, through the placental membranes into the maternal bloodstream.

As early as 1917 a German gynecologist, Hermann Kohler, had speculated that the placenta, like the corpus luteum, might also function as a temporary hormone-producing gland. But his guess—for that was all it was—was too far ahead of its time; no one among the early endocrine researchers knew how to follow it up and prove it to be either true or false. By the mid-1930s, however, the question of whether another organ took over after the corpus luteum ceased producing progesterone was a "ripe" one. And so, at McGill University in Montreal, a group of researchers—headed by Drs. Eleanor Venning, John Symonds Browne, and John Henry—began a long study of progesterone activities during pregnancy.

Their first task was to find a way of measuring just how much progesterone a woman produced at various times, both during her normal menstrual cycles and during various stages of pregnancy. If progesterone itself could have been isolated from urine, the job would have been easy. But earlier researchers had already found that progesterone was metabolized in the liver into an inactive steroid substance, pregnanediol. In 1936 Dr. Venning set out to devise a method of extracting this metabolite from urine. And when she succeeded, she and her associates had the essential tool with which to pursue their principal aim. By measuring the rate of pregnanediol *excretion*, they could quite accurately determine the otherwise unmeasurable rate of progesterone *secretion*.

Within barely a year, in fact, they were able to show that pregnanediol appeared in a normal woman's urine within twenty-four to forty-eight hours after ovulation touched off the corpus luteum's release of progesterone, that this excretion continued for ten to twelve days, and that it disappeared one to three days before the start of menstruation.

Their tests showed that if a woman became pregnant the normal daily excretion of 4 to 10 milligrams of pregnanediol, the same as during the luteal phase of the menstrual cycle, continued for between two and three months. But at that point, just as the corpus luteum became inactive, the pregnanediol level of a normal woman's urine *did not decline*. Instead, it soared. By the hundred fiftieth day of a normal pregnancy, the urinary output of pregnanediol usually reached 40 milligrams a day. By the eighth month of pregnancy, pregnanediol levels peaked at between 70 and 80 milligrams daily. Then, just before labor began, pregnanediol assays signaled a precipitate drop-off in progesterone secretion. Within twenty-four hours after delivery, and expulsion of the placenta, the excretion of pregnanediol fell to nearly zero.

These measurements, at all stages of normal pregnancy, of pregnanediol excretions not only provided a perfect picture of how the low-level progesterone output of the corpus luteum supported pregnancy while the fetus was tiny and the uterus undistended. They also proved conclusively that the placenta took over the job of producing progesterone from the corpus luteum when the fetus began its rapid growth and the muscles of the uterus had to stretch to accommodate it.

Then Drs. Venning, Browne, and Henry turned to another, but closely related, problem: the measurement of pregnanediol levels in the urine of women who were "staining" or feeling the cramps of an incipient abortion. Among these women their assays revealed not a normal second-month rise in pregnanediol excretion but a sharp drop in the output of this progesterone metabolite. On the basis of these observations they could draw only one conclusion: abortions which occurred at the time when the placenta normally assumes the functions of the corpus luteum resulted from a deficiency of progesterone brought about by a delay in this all-important takeover process.

Between 1936 and 1938, as the reports of the brilliant discoveries of Dr. Venning and her co-workers were published, two Philadelphia gynecologists had been avidly analyzing every detail of the Montreal experiments. One was fifty-eight-year-old Dr. Norris Wistar Vaux, Professor of

Obstetrics at Jefferson Medical College; the other, his obstetrical resident, twenty-six-year-old Abraham E. Rakoff. For they saw in these reports not only the answers to *why* many miscarriages occurred but also a direct lead toward a means of preventing spontaneous abortions. If one cause of abortion was indeed a delay in the placenta's assumption of its progesterone-secreting role, they reasoned, might they not be able to halt an incipient abortion by tiding the mother over the delay period with an outside progesterone supply?

They got their first chance to test this hypothesis upon a young woman already suffering the cramps of an incipient abortion, to whom they administered an injection of 10 milligrams of progesterone, a large dose in the days when progesterone cost over $200 a gram. Two days later they repeated this procedure and they continued to do so every two or three days. And it worked! Their patient's staining stopped; her cramps ceased; her uterine muscles gave up their frantic attempt to expel her fetus; and at the end of a full term, she delivered a normal baby.

But one seeming success cannot prove the effectiveness of a new therapy. The patient's cramps *might* have subsided without progesterone. Even the bed rest she enjoyed while under treatment *might* have saved her baby. And so, the professor and his resident waited—until another just-right case came along, and then another, and still another—until they had tried the new treatment on twenty-four habitual aborters.

On nine of these women, they reported in 1939, progesterone failed to prevent a miscarriage. But on fifteen others—a substantially higher percentage than could possibly be ascribed to chance or bed rest—the hormone injections were followed by a full-term or nearly full-term pregnancy and the successful delivery of a normal infant.

Soon other gynecologists in other hospitals tested the Vaux-Rakoff therapy, and some reported an even higher percentage of successes. Others experienced a greater number of failures. By 1941 the Council on Pharmacy and Chemistry of the American Medical Association analyzed all the studies that by then had been published, and came up with a Scotch verdict of "not proven." "It is indeed difficult," their report stated, "to conclude from the available data whether or not progesterone or active corpus luteum extracts are of value in the treatment of habitual or threatening abortion."

After the publication of this equivocal Council report, many physicians decided to forego using the new hormone therapy. But a number of researchers took another view, asking themselves why, if progesterone apparently halted the abortion process so effectively in *some* cases, did it seem to fail so dismally in others. One of these men was Dr. Arpad Csapo, a physician at the University of Budapest who had studied the effects of hormones upon muscle contraction under the guidance of Nobel Laureate biochemist Albert Szent-Gyorgyi.

In this country Dr. Csapo joined Drs. George Corner and S. R. M. Reynolds, at the Carnegie Institution's endocrinology laboratory in Baltimore, in an attempt to identify the hormones responsible for controlling the actions of the muscles of the uterus. Through a long series of animal experiments they found that it is estrogen that induces the strong uterine muscle contractions that expel the embryo from the uterus; that one of progesterone's functions is to block this estrogen action and thus inhibit labor until the fetus is mature and the right moment for delivery arrives.

As Dr. Csapo vividly decribes it, "Estrogen primes the gun, so to speak, and progesterone blocks it from firing. Throughout normal pregnancy the muscles are ready to explode on twenty-four hours' notice, but they cannot fire until the gun is cocked; that is to say, until the progesterone block is withdrawn."

This finding went far toward explaining both the successes and the failures of progesterone therapy when used to prevent spontaneous abortion. Injected progesterone, for example, takes about sixteen hours to exert its effects. Thus it cannot help if it is administered too late—that is, after an abortion is already well started. But given early enough to a woman whose placenta is producing *some* progesterone on its own, it may supplement that placental secretion and thus tide a patient over.

Furthermore, the 10- and 20-milligram doses administered in the early anti-abortion experiments were too small to halt most incipient abortions. But when Dr. Eleanor Delfs, of The Johns Hopkins Hospital, administered 100- and 200-milligram injections to a woman who had had six miscarriages, her patient was able to carry two successive babies to full-term.

Progesterone had another drawback. Since it was orally inactive, it had to be administered by injection. And when massive and frequent doses were used, these injections often evoked painful local reactions and sometimes caused the development of persistent cysts at the injection sites. Hence, while many physicians did use progesterone as a weapon against miscarriage, in the late 1940s and early 1950s, most did so reluctantly and usually as a last resort.

This situation, however, changed drastically when chemists developed the 19-nor steroid hormones. Unlike progesterone, these synthetic compounds could be administered orally and, milligram for milligram, were many times as active as progesterone.

Fittingly, it was Dr. Abraham Rakoff who was one of the first to appreciate the abortion-preventing potentialities of these new steroids. In the years since he and Dr. Vaux had first used progesterone to halt an impending miscarriage, he had won wide recognition as a gifted endocrine researcher and appointment as Clinical Professor of Obstetric and Gynecologic Endocrinology at Jefferson Medical College.

Between 1956 and 1958 he used Enovid to treat thirty-eight patients, of whom eighteen were habitual aborters who had either never been able to carry a baby to term or had a record of three or more consecutive abortions. The other twenty were women who already had suffered one or two miscarriages and who were now threatened with imminent abortion.

All of these patients received 10-milligram Enovid pills every day, beginning from seven to ten days after their first missed menstrual period. During their second month of pregnancy this dosage was increased to 20 milligrams daily. If staining started, the dosage was raised to 40 milligrams per day until blood flow ceased.

Among the habitual aborters the pre-treatment fetal salvage rate had been only 37 percent; their sixty-two previous pregnancies had resulted in the birth of only twenty-three living babies. But under Dr. Rakoff's new Enovid regimen the salvage rate rose to 83 percent; fourteen of the eighteen habitual aborters delivered healthy infants. Of the twenty women facing threatened abortions, twelve overcame their difficulties under Enovid treatment, for a fetal salvage rate of 60 percent.

Saving the Unborn /*179*

"One advantage of this compound," Dr. Rakoff reported, "is that it may be given to pregnant women in reasonably large doses, in a most convenient form and with few side effects . . . a truly great advance. In this group of patients I have not had a single complaint of nausea nor any instance in which therapy had to be discontinued because of side effects."

Many other clinical researchers soon confirmed Dr. Rakoff's experience. Dr. Edward E. Napp, Clinical Professor of Obstetrics and Gynecology at New York Medical College, reported on the treatment of six habitual aborters with Enovid, five of whom delivered full-term infants. At the Brookline Reproductive Study Center, Drs. John Rock and Celso Ramon Garcia used Enovid prophylactically on a series of forty-eight women, who, in ninety-five previous pregnancies, had managed to carry only thirty babies through to term, for a fetal salvage rate of only 31.6 percent. Yet under Enovid therapy, the fetal salvage rate among these same women rose to 57 percent. "In other words," these researchers reported, "the percentage of salvage of pregnancies in identical matings was nearly doubled when Enovid was administered."

At St. Elizabeth Hospital in Lincoln, Nebraska, a team headed by Dr. Samuel T. Thierstein used three different synthetic progestin-like agents on a total of 166 patients, each with a record of from one to seven previous abortions. A control group of eighty similar habitual aborters received the traditional bed rest and sedation but no hormone medication. Among these controls, only twenty-five live births were recorded; a fetal salvage rate of barely 31 percent.

"All these progesterone-like hormones," Dr. Thierstein reported, "are excellent in preventing abortion." Of the forty women treated with Norlutin, the 19-nor steroid known as norethesterone, twenty carried their pregnancies to term, for a fetal salvage rate of 50 percent. Of sixty-six habitual aborters treated with Delalutin, chemically 17-hydroxyprogesterone 17-caproate, forty-two achieved full-term pregnancies; a fetal salvage of nearly 64 percent. And among the group of sixty-one patients treated with Enovid, forty-eight gave birth to normal infants at term; a salvage rate of nearly 79 percent.

One of the most interesting of these studies was that conducted by Drs. Alvin F. Goldfarb and Doung D. Gongsakdi at the Fetal Salvage Clinic of the Jefferson Medical College Hospital. To 77 women who had previously suffered a total of 340 miscarriages, they administered 10 milligrams of Enovid daily through the fourth month of gestation and then increased the daily dose to 20 milligrams through the eighth month. Among habitual aborters, the fetal salvage rate rose from 48 percent to 60 percent. Among repeated aborters, 43 percent of whose previous pregnancies had ended in miscarriage, the salvage rate with Enovid therapy was over 78 percent. And among women who had previously suffered repeated premature labor, the salvage rate under hormone treatment rose to 100 percent.

As numerous other researchers published reports of similar studies of large groups of women successfully protected by Enovid and other progesterone-like compounds against hormone deficiency abortions, the use of these agents became widely accepted. Then in 1960 Dr. Lawson Wilkins, of the Division of Pediatric Endocrinology of The Johns Hopkins University School of Medicine, published, in the *Journal of the American Medical Association*, a report on instances of masculinization noted among female infants, almost all born to mothers who had received hormone therapy during their pregnancies. From his own case records and from those of other researchers he gathered a total of 101 such cases, some mild, some pronounced. Fifteen had occurred under the administration of testosterone or other known androgens; thirty-four had followed treatment with ethenyl-testosterone; thirty-five had occurred after therapy with the mildly androgenic 19-nor steroid Norlutin; ten cases had been noted among the babies of mothers who had received no steroids at all; and in a single instance, fetal masculinization had been reported following the administration of Enovid. (In a later publication the author of this report, Dr. Melvin M. Grumbach, stated that this incident was probably coincidental rather than a result of Enovid treatment.)

Compared with the very large number of pregnant women who have received hormone treatment during pregnancy, the incidence of enlargement of the clitoris or other evidence of masculization in their babies is extremely low. Many physicians, and certainly most women facing abortion, would regard the small risk as well worth taking to save the life of an unborn child. Nonetheless, Dr. Wilkins' study served the very useful purpose of alerting all physicians to this element of possible risk and to the extent of the risk involved in the use of different hormones. Thus, both because Enovid was cited as masculinizing in only one instance (and that a dubious one) and because it is estrogenic and has no androgenic effects on test animals, this 19-nor steroid has become the progestational agent of choice for the treatment of recurrent or threatened abortion.

It is not a "miracle drug," if indeed there are any such. It cannot prevent miscarriages *not* due to hormonal deficiency. But in cases of demonstrated hormone deficiency it does offer physicians and their abortion-threatened patients a greater prospect of a full-term delivery, with greater safety, than any other agent now available.

11

•

A NEW WEAPON

AGAINST MENSTRUAL

AILMENTS

•

Save for the common cold, no human ill strikes more often than the painful and debilitating disorders of menstruation. Almost all women are afflicted, at times, by one or more of these disorders. And for all too many millions, only pregnancy provides temporary surcease from the agonizing

cramps or the prolonged or excessive bleeding they otherwise experience at every dreaded menstrual period.

Down through the centuries physicians, and medicine
men before them, have tried to prevent or cure these disorders. Until recent decades almost all such efforts failed, because too little was known about the complex processes by
which nature regulates the normal menstrual cycle and even
less was understood about the influences that turn normal
menstrual patterns into wildly disturbed ones. Thus physicians could offer suffering women little more than the advice
to take to their beds until their hemorrhagic bleeding
stopped and deaden their pain with such anodynes as aspirin,
codeine, or "female complaint" elixirs, which were effective,
if at all, only in direct ratio to their alcoholic content.

But with the upsurge of endocrine research in the early
years of this century, physiologists and clinicians launched
new attempts to unravel the mysteries of the menstrual
cycle. At first their progress was painfully slow. Hundreds
of experiments and careful studies of the menstrual cycles of
thousands of patients yielded only seemingly unrelated bits
of data. By the mid 1930s, however, researchers had accumulated enough of these bits and pieces of new knowledge
to assemble them into an almost complete picture.

The normal menstrual cycle, they had learned, was
governed by a group of ovarian and pituitary hormones
operating in an exquisitely timed sequence. At the start of
each such cycle the pituitary gland releases a hormone that
stimulates the growth of a number of follicles on the surface
of the ovaries. These in turn begin to produce a second
hormone, estradiol, which initiates a rebuilding of the lining
of the uterus which had been shed, down to its lowermost
layer of cells, during menstruation.

By about the fourteenth day of the cycle the estrogen

level in the blood has risen sufficiently to "notify" the
pituitary to cut down its output of follicle-stimulating hormone and to release, instead, a lutenizing hormone. Under
the influence of this second gonadotropin, one ovarian
follicle ruptures and releases an egg cell, which passes
through the Fallopian tubes and, if fertilized, nests, or
nidates, in the new uterine lining.

Now, within the ruptured follicle sac, a temporary endocrine gland—the corpus luteum—begins to pour forth a
second ovarian hormone progesterone. This exerts a smoth-
ering effect on the remaining unruptured follicles, halting
their growth so that no further eggs will be released. At the
same time, carried to the uterus by the bloodstream, progesterone performs two other essential tasks: It stimulates a
second stage of growth in the womb's lining, preparing it
to nourish the newly nidated ovum. It also damps down the
rhythmic contractions of the uterine muscles, so that the
ovum will not be dislodged or damaged.

If fertilization fails to occur, the thickened lining of the
womb must be discarded so that a new cycle of preparation
for pregnancy can begin. Nature accomplishes this by allowing the corpus luteum to degenerate and thus, quite
abruptly, end its output of progesterone. As this occurs the
muscles of the uterus are no longer inhibited from rhythmic
contractions. As these muscles go into action the womb's
lining—denied its progesterone support—begins to break up.
Together with a quantity of blood from its ruptured capillaries this macerated tissue is sloughed off through the vagina
in the final phase of the cycle, menstruation.

From this new picture of the normal menstrual cycle
physicians also gained a clearer understanding of the underlying causes of many menstrual disturbances. In many

women, most of the time, the correct sequence of hormone actions occurs with an almost clock-like precision. But the entire long chain of events is obviously vulnerable to disruption by any excess or deficiency in the output of any of the essential hormones. Thus, in the hope of compensating for deficiencies of hormone secretion and of overcoming endocrine imbalances, gynecologists began to administer hormone extracts—and later, pure hormones—to women suffering from menstrual disorders.

Much of the work of these pioneers had to be based, of necessity, upon trial-and-error methods. Clinical researchers injected estrogens, gonadotropic hormones, or even androgens into gallant volunteers willing to try anything that seemed to offer even a long-shot chance of ending their periodic pain or their monthly hemorrhagic bleeding. Soon each of these therapies had ardent advocates, who cited apparent successes, and equally vocal opponents, who pointed out the high proportion of women to whom treatment gave no relief.

The nearest approach to an all-out success was achieved with progesterone, which, when administered during the two weeks prior to menstruation, prevented acute menstrual pain in about 50 percent of the patients treated. But since such relief was achieved only for the menses immediately following treatment, few women were willing to undergo— and even fewer could afford—the repeated painful courses of injections that were essential if they were to obtain long-term freedom from menstrual cramps.

Thus the first high hopes of ending menstrual disturbances by hormonal replacement therapy faded. Many physicians reverted to prescribing bed rest and analgesics for all but the most severe cases of menstrual disorder. And even to these women they tended to offer hormone treatment only as a last resort and to warn them that the odds were great against obtaining more than partial or temporary relief.

But when Dr. John Rock began his attempts to relieve infertility by the cyclic administration of norethynodrel, he noted that the new synthetic steroid had a highly desirable "side effect" in addition to its ability to inhibit ovulation. A number of his volunteer patients who had previously experienced painful menstrual cramps or excessive bleeding now reported that when they ended a twenty-day course of pill-taking, their ensuing menstrual period was relatively painless and they no longer bled excessively. Thus, he and Dr. Celso Ramon Garcia began a series of clinical investigations of Enovid's effects on women suffering from a wide variety of menstrual disorders.

At about the same time, similar studies with Enovid were undertaken by a number of other, highly qualified gynecologists. As a result, within the span of barely three years, the treatment of menstrual disorders underwent a series of revolutionary changes as physicians all over the world began to use the new orally effective progestin-estrogen combination to relieve conditions that had stubbornly resisted all previous modes of treatment.

One of the first to test the usefulness of the 19-nor steroids in the treatment of excessive uterine bleeding was Dr. Anna L. Southam, Associate Professor of Obstetrics and Gynecology at the Columbia University College of Physicians and Surgeons. Long experienced in gynecological research, she approached this problem with the caution, tough-mindedness, and inherent skepticism of a true scientist. For her first trials, for example, she selected fifteen patients with abnormal uterine bleeding associated with lack of ovulation.

All had repeatedly experienced excessive loss of blood during their menstrual periods—what physicians term hypermenorrhea or menorrhagia. A number had also experienced frightening episodes of metrorrhagia, or hemorrhagic bleeding at times other than their menstrual periods.

"Eight of these patients were bleeding profusely at the time Enovid was given," Dr. Southam reported early in 1957 to a research symposium. "Bleeding was satisfactorily controlled in six and in two further curettage was required. In all fifteen patients, following withdrawal bleeding after the initial course of therapy, menorrhagia and metrorrhagia were well controlled with 10 milligrams of Enovid for 21 days."

Then Dr. Southam tested the new drug on four patients with excessive uterine bleeding associated *with* ovulation, in all of whom blood losses had been so great as to cause marked postmenstrual anemia, evidenced by a sharp drop in the number of their hemoglobin or red blood cells. "Three of these patients," she reported, "responded well when 10 milligrams of Enovid were given for 21 days. Response was less satisfactory in another patient treated for only the last 14 days of the cycle. Menstruation following Enovid is moderate in amount and is not associated with a significant fall in hemoglobin."

After extending her studies to a larger series of patients, Dr. Southam reported that she had found the 19-nor steroids to be "dramatic hemostatic agents [that] will decrease profuse anovulatory bleeding within a few hours and arrest it completely within 24 to 48 hours. The patient can then be kept amenorrheic by continued therapy until withdrawal bleeding is desired. The amount of drug given is an important factor in adequate control; 10 milligrams per day is sometimes successful, 20 milligrams per day is generally routinely successful but occasionally 30 milligrams per day may be needed. I have never found it necessary to use more. Withdrawal bleeding, when it occurs, is usually not profuse or prolonged."

At the Brookline Reproductive Study Center, Drs. Rock and Garcia treated a group of fifty women in whom hormonal imbalances had completely disrupted normal menstrual cycles. In these women not only the timing of menstruation but its duration and the volume of its blood flow had become utterly unpredictable. Occasionally they experienced a normal menstrual period. But the cycles which followed would almost always be shorter or longer than normal and the blood flow, when those aberrant cycles ended, would usually be abnormal in both volume and duration.

By the cyclic use of Enovid, Drs. Rock and Garcia were able to help almost all of these women achieve a regular timing of menstruation. And in 76 percent this correction of timing was also accompanied by the re-establishment of a normal volume and duration of blood flow.

In a parallel study by the same investigators women with properly timed but excessive and prolonged menstrual bleeding were also put on Enovid regimens. After such treatment 89 percent of their post-treatment cycles were normal in all observable respects.

The observations of Drs. Southam, Rock, and Garcia were soon confirmed by studies conducted by such other distinguished clinical researchers as Dr. Maxwell Roland of New York's Albert Einstein College of Medicine, Dr. Carl G. Heller, Associate Professor of Endocrinology at the University of Oregon Medical School, Dr. Robert B. Greenblatt, Professor of Endocrinology at the Medical College of Georgia, and Dr. C. Herman Weinberg, senior gynecologist at the Touro Infirmary of New Orleans. Thus, when the Council on Drugs of the American Medical Association reported on the therapeutic applications of Enovid, this extremely cautious and conservative board was able to declare: "This progestin-estrogen combination is extremely useful in controlling the symptoms of dysfunctional uterine bleeding. . . . Anovulatory hemorrhages can be rapidly controlled . . . and intermittent therapy can prevent subsequent hemorrhages."

One of the most puzzling and refractory of all menstrual disturbances is the condition physicians call dysmenorrhea, but which its victims describe more bluntly as "crippling cramps." Numerous surveys—conducted in girls' schools, among housewives, and among female factory and office workers—have shown that, regardless of age and occupation, more than one third of all women are afflicted with dysmenorrhea during at least some of their menstrual periods. But tens of thousands are incapacitated for from two to six days every month by such recurrent griping pains. Often their cramps start days before the actual onset of menstruation. Frequently they radiate from the pelvic region to involve the entire abdomen and spread down the thighs.

Most victims of menstrual cramps have managed to "get through" their periods by dosing themselves with analgesics. But for many the pain has been so severe and persistent that doctors, in the past, have often felt compelled to attempt heroic measures in the hope of providing these patients some relief. Thus, operations to dilate the cervical canal at the entrance to the uterus were frequently performed. When these failed to bring relief, some physicians resorted to injections of alcohol into the pelvic nerves or even to an actual severance of the nerves leading to the ovaries.

Reluctant to take such drastic measures, however, physicians everywhere welcomed the isolation and production of progesterone in the late 1930s. They recognized that no matter how widely menstrual cramps varied in the time of their onset and in the pattern of their spread through the body, they often seemed to originate in abnormally forceful contractions of the muscles of the uterus. Thus they developed the hypothesis that such abnormal contractions resulted from a progesterone deficiency, which was thought to be caused in turn by a premature degeneration of the corpus luteum. It therefore seemed logical to try to relieve this deficiency by replacement therapy with progesterone injections.

As we have already seen, however, the high cost and the pain of such injections tended to restrict their use to only the severest cases. Even then, results were often disappointing. But when the 19-nor steroids were first used to control excessive menstrual bleeding, clinical investigators were delighted to find that they also relieved the cramps often associated with such bleeding. Thus, it was inevitable that attempts would be made to use these new, easily administered, less costly synthetic progestins in the treatment of patients whose menstrual cramps were not associated with profuse bleeding.

One of the first to do so was Dr. C. Herman Weinberg. For a series of seventeen patients, ten of whom had not responded satisfactorily to previous therapy with other drugs, he prescribed Enovid in nightly 10-milligram doses, from the fifth to the twenty-fifth day of their cycles. Regardless of the previous duration or severity of their symptoms, every one of these patients achieved marked and often complete relief.

Typical was the case of Miss T. K., a twenty-four-year-old salesclerk, who had suffered from painful menstruation for fully ten years. Various medications and even a dilatation and curettage operation had afforded her no relief. Every month, cramps had forced her to be absent from work for at least the first two days of her period. But after she had completed just one course of cyclic therapy she experienced, for the first time in a decade, a menstrual period completely free from pain. And when her treatment with Enovid was discontinued after four months, she remained free of dysmenorrhea through many months of subsequent observation.

Numerous other investigators soon found that they could duplicate the results obtained by Dr. Weinberg even though they reduced daily doses of the pill to only 5 milligrams. Since then, although the mechanism responsible for the prevention of cramps when ovulation is inhibited is still not understood, thousands of physicians have found that with the pill they can, in almost every instance, effect dramatic and continued relief from menstrual cramps.

More than two thousand years ago, Greek physicians recognized that ordinarily calm women frequently became high strung and irritable during the days preceding menstruation. To indicate the physical origin of this nervous condition they named it hysteria, after their language's word for the womb—*hystera*. It was not until 1931, in fact, that the more descriptive, if less euphonious term "premenstrual tension" was coined. It is undoubtedly the most common of all disorders related to menstruation, affecting an estimated 70 percent of all women with varying degrees of severity.

The first manifestation of the disorder, six to eight days before the start of menstruation, is a vague feeling of mounting tension which develops into marked physical unrest and constant irritability. Its victims may not recognize the change they are undergoing, but others around them cannot help but note their tendency to show extreme annoyance over trifles and to give vent to unreasonable emotional outbursts. As the time of menstruation nears, many women experience causeless crying spells, increasing insomnia, dizziness, a painful tingling of the breasts, or constant headaches. In teen-agers acne often worsens at this time and they may become more susceptible to allergic reactions. A number of studies have shown that the incidence of both suicide and crimes of violence among women is much higher in the week before menstruation than at any other time.

Until recent years physicians had no direct means of controlling the underlying cause of premenstrual tension except for the prescription of low-sodium diets or diuretics to offset the tendency toward salt-and-water retention found in some patients at this time. But in 1956, in the course of investigating the effects of Enovid on other menstrual disorders, Dr. Carl G. Heller noted that the 19-nor steroids also relieved concurrent premenstrual tension states. He therefore extended his experiments to a group of twenty women, whom he treated for at least three menstrual cycles. "Premenstrual tension," he reported, "was abolished or significantly alleviated in each patient during each treated cycle as well as in the post-treatment cycle. This asymptomatic state may remain for upward of six cycles." On a similar group of patients with a history of premenstrual tension, Dr. C. Herman Weinberg obtained good results by administering the drug for just seven days before the expected menstruation.

● ● ●

In their early experiments on the use of norethynodrel to suppress ovulation, Drs. Pincus and Rock adopted a twenty-day treatment schedule so that menstruation would begin on the twenty-eighth or twenty-ninth day and thus maintain what women regard as a normal span between periods. When, however, clinicians began using Enovid to control excessive uterine bleeding, they often felt that a more prolonged delay of menstrual flow would permit a greater degree of recovery from post-hemorrhagic anemia. They soon found that the time of menstruation could be delayed or advanced at will, simply by shortening or extending the pill-taking schedule. In the *Journal of the American Medical Association,* for example, Dr. Robert Greenblatt reported that menstruation could be delayed by starting a course of daily doses of 19-nor steroids as late as the twenty-fourth day of the cycle.

There are many medical reasons for such postponement of menses: in order to avoid anemia when major surgery is planned, for example, or to permit uninterrupted treatment of vaginal infections and other conditions involving the pelvic organs. But many physicians also advance or delay menstruation dates for valid social reasons: to avoid an enforced postponement of the date of a marriage; in instances where vacations would otherwise be marred; to permit girl athletes to participate in scheduled competitions; to allow theatrical performers, opera singers, and ballet dancers to meet planned engagements.

12

•

BETTER PILLS AT

LOWER COST

•

In May of 1960, after norethynodrel had weathered nearly six full years of clinical testing, the Federal Food and Drug Administration permitted its marketing for prescription use as Enovid, the first physiological oral contraceptive. At that time the longest series of clinical trials had been with women who took 10 milligrams daily. The marketing "license" was therefore quite properly limited by the FDA to the 10-milligram pill. At that dosage the retail price for the twenty pills required during a month was over $11, or more than fifty-five cents per pill.

While the new drug was hailed as a tremendous advance over all earlier types of contraceptives, there were many who feared that the price of the pills might severely limit their acceptance and use, particularly among women in the lower economic groups. But despite its relatively high cost hundreds of thousands of women quickly decided that they preferred the pill over all other types of contraceptive, because of its safety and its proven effectiveness, and because it permitted them to completely separate their precautions against pregnancy from the time of sexual relations. Even the economically disadvantaged "voted" for the pill. At Planned Parenthood Clinics throughout the country, where seven contraceptive methods were available, a majority of women chose the pill although it was the only contraceptive for which the clinics made a charge to families on relief or public assistance.

This unexpectedly rapid acceptance of Enovid by great numbers of women—and improved production techniques—soon permitted the makers of the new pill to put through a 30-percent price reduction. By 1961 the retail cost of a month's supply of the 10-milligram pills dropped to about $7.50.

Meanwhile, ever since 1958, clinical researchers had been experimenting with reduced dosage levels as a means of minimizing side effects. As sufficient evidence accumulated that the new steroid was equally effective in a 5-milligram daily dose and caused even fewer and milder side effects, the FDA permitted physicians to prescribe the smaller pills for contraceptive use. Thus, by 1962, the retail cost of a month's supply of Enovid fell to about $3.50 and several million additional women began to rely upon the pill.

Already under way, however, were further clinical trials at still lower dosage levels. Early in 1964, after these had demonstrated that 2.5-milligram pills were fully effective in preventing pregnancy, the FDA approved the marketing of this still smaller daily dose under the brand name Enovid-E. In less than four years clinical research and improved production methods thus made possible an 80-percent reduction in the cost of oral contraception—from over $11 a month to about $2.25.

At this point, however, the drive to reduce both side effects and cost to the consumer came up against a hard scientific fact. When research physicians attempted to use Enovid in doses at or below the 2-milligram level, they found that many women experienced some breakthrough bleeding.

That some such barrier to the further lowering of Enovid's dosage eventually would be reached had long been anticipated. That was why, in fact, chemists at the G. D. Searle research laboratories had launched an intensive quest for more potent progestins almost as soon as Enovid's contraceptive efficacy had been established in 1955. Great numbers of both old and newly synthesized steroids were evaluated biologically for their possible utility as ovulation inhibitors. Several score were found to possess some anti-ovulatory potency. Until 1959, however, all of these compounds had proved to be either of relatively low potency or had displayed other activities which made them inappropriate for use as contraceptives.

In that year, with the ink still wet on his Ph.D. in organic chemistry, Dr. Paul Klimstra joined the Searle research staff and was assigned to work under Dr. Colton's guidance on the preparation of a series of 19-nor steroid derivatives. Dr.

Colton had already demonstrated that certain side chain modifications at the number-17 position tended to reduce androgenic activity in these compounds. Dr Klimstra soon found one particular side chain change which almost completely eliminated androgenicity.

Next Klimstra was assigned to the further exploration of another phenomenon which had been noted by Dr. Colton and others: that some alterations of the side chains attached to the number-3 position in these steroids tended to give them a substantially prolonged or enhanced activity. Once again the young chemist succeeded in synthesizing a compound which exhibited this desired effect to a greater degree than did earlier members of this series.

Now, after extended discussions, Drs. Colton and Klimstra decided that it might be worth-while to attempt to synthesize a steroid molecule incorporating both of these modifications. It proved to be an exceedingly difficult job. But after a discouraging number of failures Dr. Klimstra finally accomplished his purpose, producing some three hundred grams of a compound which was given the serial number SC-11800 and sent to the Division of Biological Research to be put through routine preliminary activity-screening tests.

A month passed. Then, one morning, a stranger to Klimstra walked into his lab, introduced himself as Dr. Elton of Biological Research, and said, "You seem to have a fairly interesting compound in this SC-11800. But we've used up almost all of it on the first screening. How fast can you put together some more of it for us?"

Dr. Klimstra still cannot remember just how he answered his unexpected visitor. But he does know that even before the door closed upon the departing Dr. Elton, he was excitedly re-rigging the apparatus with which he first had cooked up his new compound. And this time there were no slip-ups. Within a few days he had put together enough and more of SC-11800 to let the biologists perform every last test in their books.

When Drs. Victor Drill, Richard Elton, Ehard Nutting, and a corps of assistants put this "interesting" compound through these rigorous tests, it was found to exert a series of

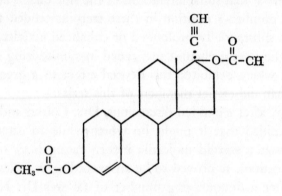

SC-11800
Progestin of Ovulen ®

unique hormonal effects. As Drs. Colton and Klimstra had hoped, it proved to have an extremely low level of androgenicity. Injected beneath the skin of test rabbits, it proved less than twice as potent as progesterone in inhibiting ovulation—a disappointing result. But when it was administered by mouth, its ovulation-inhibiting activity turned out to be forty times as great as that of progesterone and four to five times as high as that of norethynodrel.

Thus, in August of 1961, after its safety had been demonstrated by year-long chronic-toxicity studies on dogs and rats, SC-11800 was submitted to Drs. Pincus, Garcia, Paniagua, and John Shepard for initial studies on small groups of human volunteers in San Juan, Puerto Rico.

First, to twenty-two such women, they gave either 1-milligram or 2-milligram daily doses of SC-11800 to determine whether the new agent—which had been given the generic name ethynodiol diacetate—would inhibit ovulation in humans at these low dosage levels. When this test proved completely successful they enlisted more than a hundred additional volunteers for a long-term study of side effects. Through a total of 662 menstrual cycles the 1-milligram pills not only proved their ability to prevent ovulation just as effectively as larger doses of norethynodrel; they also provided better protection against "staining" or breakthrough bleeding and evoked fewer reports of side effect reactions.

"We have found ethynodiol diacetate to be a potent anti-fertility agent, with minimal side effects, when it is administered orally in low daily dosage," these investigators reported in 1962 in *Science*. "Because of the low dosage regimen, this drug may be not only physiologically safer than others but also more economical."

Over the next two years further extensive clinical trials of ethynodiol diacetate were conducted by more than a score of research teams in the continental United States and in Great Britain, Mexico, and Australia. Dr. Edward T. Tyler, Medical Director of the Los Angeles Planned Parenthood Centers, for example, studied a group of 191 patients who used the new contraceptive for a total of 3,162 cycles. Not one of these patients became pregnant and side effects were fewer and milder than with earlier contraceptives.

Dr. E. G. Holmstrom, of the Department of Obstetrics and Gynecology of the Southern California Permanente

Medical Group, treated 473 patients with ethynodiol for a total of 8,457 cycles. He, too, reported the new compound highly effective as a contraceptive and with a very low incidence of side effects.

Putting the new steroid to an even more severe test, Dr. Charles E. Flowers of the University of North Carolina supplied it to a group of women of limited education who had been unable to make effective use of conventional contraceptives. Among 179 such patients, observed through 478 cycles, not a single pregnancy was experienced while they took the 1-milligram tablets.

From the Department of Obstetrics and Gynecology of the Norfolk, Virginia, General Hospital, Drs. William C. and Mason C. Andrews reported on the use of the new contraceptive by 288 patients in 2,429 cycles of exposure to pregnancy. "The most significant advantage of this compound," they stated in the *Journal of Fertility and Sterility*, "is that, with increased effectiveness at lower dosage, there has been an appreciable lowering of side effects. The side effects encountered with the basic Enovid combinations are usually mild and transient, but with ethynodiol diacetate they are less frequent and even milder and more transient. No pregnancies have occurred while on the regimen. Of seven patients who stopped to become pregnant, five conceived in the first two months."

Surveying the reports of fifteen American studies involving more than three thousand women who used ethynodiol diacetate for from one to fifty-three cycles, Dr. Tyler declared, "Tolerance is . . . very good and in doses of 1 mg. of this progestin, the effectiveness is excellent. No pregnancies were reported in the total of almost forty-four thousand cycles!"

In addition to clinical field trials of ethynodiol diacetate, in the United States and elsewhere, a vast amount of experience in the use of this steroid has been gained by physicians in Great Britain. In that country, where all clinical trials of contraceptives are conducted under the auspices of a central body, The Council for the Investigation of Fertility Control, the prescription of this new contraceptive, under the brand name Ovulen, has been permitted since late 1963. Thus, over the last two years, tens of thousands of British women have been successfully utilizing this second-generation pill. Since 1964 Ovulen has also been available in Australia and South Africa.

As this is written, a New Drug Application, which would permit the marketing of Ovulen in the United States, is pending before the Federal Food and Drug Administration. The reduced amount of the chemical in the tablet may lead to greater economies for the patient who receives an Ovulen prescription from the doctor.

13

•

PHYSICIANS AND THE
PUBLIC'S HEALTH

•

Nearly a century ago, in 1873, a fiery-eyed zealot named Anthony Comstock descended upon Washington as the "chief special agent" of a vest pocket organization he called The Society for the Suppression of Vice. Armed with a thick portfolio of pornography he sought to shock the U. S. Congress into passing a bill ostensibly designed to prevent the country from being debauched by a flood of obscene publications.

By deliberately securing the introduction of his measure late in the session, he managed to get it past the Senate without any debate and past the House of Representatives without even a roll call. In fact, in their haste to adjourn and get home, the members of both houses gave so little study to the Comstock Act that few realized that its promoter had slipped into it clauses which made it a criminal offense to import or mail not only pornographic pictures and obscene publications, but also "any article of medicine for the prevention of conception." Even scientific discussions or descriptions of contraceptive devices or methods were banned under the bill's all-encompassing definition of "obscene literature."

Over the next few years Comstock carried his whirlwind anti-obscenity campaigns into all the state legislatures. Again, as in Congress, most of the lawmakers did not take his bills seriously enough to bother to read the small type. To them Comstock was just another professional gadfly who might cost them votes if he wasn't appeased. So they sang out their hearty "Ayes" and went on to the more important business of voting school bonds or regulating railroads or levying taxes. In the end Comstock and his little road company of fanatics managed to coerce every legislature save that of New Mexico into passing obscenity laws which could be construed to restrict the dissemination of contraceptive information or the distribution of contraceptive supplies. More than half of these statutes, like the Federal Act, expressly included contraceptives within their ban. In Connecticut even the *use* of a means of contraception was made a crime subject to punishment by fine or even imprisonment.

For a time, little attempt was made to put into effect these anti-birth control sections of the new acts. But when, with indefatigable zeal, Comstock contrived to secure his own appointment as a special agent of the Post Office Department to supervise the enforcement of his law, the thinking public—and especially the medical profession—began to realize what heavy shackles had been imposed upon them. The editors of medical journals, for example, discovered that entire issues of their publications could be confiscated by the postal authorities if they contained even a single scientific reference to the subject of contraception. When Dr. William H. Cary devised one of the first contraceptive jellies, he could find no medical journal whose editor dared risk publishing its formula. Publishers had to eliminate all reference to contraceptive techniques from medical textbooks or risk their confiscation. Even a doctor who ordered a textbook from abroad could, under the broad provisions of the Federal Act, incur upon himself a jail sentence of up to ten years for "taking or causing to be taken from the mail any such package."

As citizens, doctors resented the infringement by these laws of their rights of freedom of speech and of the press. As scientists and as the educators of future physicians, they resented equally the blockade which Comstockery imposed upon the exchange of scientific knowledge. But it was as men dedicated to the protection of the people's health that physicians felt compelled to oppose Comstock's laws which, in effect, forced them to deny instruction in contraception even to women whose very lives would be endangered by another pregnancy.

Thus, long before any organized birth control movement developed, many doctors boldly wrote and many medical journals boldly published discussions of contraception that clearly challenged state and Federal authorities to bring court cases against them so that the constitutionality of the statutes could be tested.

As early as 1882, for example, the *Michigan Medical News* published an article by Dr. O. E. Herrick in which he advocated the teaching of contraception to husbands and wives as the best means of preventing the widespread resort to abortionists (or self-induced abortions) with its inevitable risks of injury, infection, or death. In subsequent months the same journal printed dozens of letters from other physicians who discussed both Dr. Herrick's article *and* the relative merits of various means of contraception and thus, in effect, offered to join their colleague in any test of their right to open discussion.

In 1888 the editor of the *Medical and Surgical Reporter*, of Philadelphia, published an editorial inviting his readers to take part in a similar challenge symposium, an invitation quickly accepted by physicians from every section of the country. Dr. W. R. D. Blackwood indignantly reminded his colleagues of the "wretched, broken-down women whose lives have been wrecked because they have become mere machines for reproduction. To me," he added, "the matter reduces itself to a choice between fœticide and prevention. The one is an indefensible crime—the other a necessity." From Cameron, Texas, Dr. Thomas A. Pope declared that "Prevention is a question the medical profession will have to face. . . . From the medical standpoint too frequent childbearing causes the weaning of the preceding child, thus increasing death hazards. . . . Knowledge of the prevention of conception would undoubtedly reduce the maternal death rate." Numerous other physicians, including some who opposed contraception, joined the symposium, both to contribute their views and to enroll their names as men unwilling to accept any denial of the right of free scientific discussion.

Neither of these two initial invitations to a court test of the Comstock Act was accepted by the postal authorities, and from 1890 onward—with their right to write freely reestablished, by default as it were—numerous doctors published articles on contraception and its techniques in more than a score of medical journals, although both the authors and the editors knew that they were deliberately risking prosecution in doing so.

Meanwhile the physicians' struggle to establish their right to speak about, write about, *and* to teach contraception to their patients began to take on a new form. In 1912 the revered Dr. Abraham Jacobi deliberately attacked the taboos of the Comstock laws in his inaugural address as President of the American Medical Association. He reminded his audience of the requirement in their code of medical ethics—that in a delivery-room crisis, the physician must try to save the mother's life even if this means the loss of the unborn child. Then he added, "If we have no right to demand a sacrifice of the mother for the sake of the child, neither have we the right to demand sacrifices which . . . shorten and cripple a woman's life." But he did not limit his plea for the prescription of contraceptives solely to instances in which further childbearing would directly endanger the mother's life or death. Contraception, he declared, "benefits the parents, it is decidedly beneficial to society, and *it is even more merciful to the unborn and unconceived creature which it frequently saves from a life of misery*."

Thus, through its elected leader, medicine *as a profession* first raised a clear voice against the shackles which the Comstock laws imposed upon medical practice. From then on bold individual physicians and brave individual editors no longer had to struggle solely as individuals. Instead, through local, state, and specialist societies, and through the A.M.A. itself, the medical profession worked ever more intensively to eliminate all legislative barriers to the doctor's right to prescribe contraceptives.

When, in 1916, the nurse, Margaret Sanger, was arrested and jailed for opening the country's first birth control clinic, doctors as well as laymen gave both financial and vocal support to her defense. Later, when Mrs. Sanger organized the American Birth Control League, numerous physicians served on its National Committee, on the Boards and Medical Advisory Committees of its local branches, and as medical directors of its growing chain of clinics—even though in so doing they risked arrest and the loss of their licenses to practice medicine.

In 1925 the Section on Obstetrics, Gynecology and Abdominal Surgery of the American Medical Association debated and decisively passed a strong resolution calling for the alteration of existing laws wherever necessary so that physicians could legally give contraceptive information to their patients in the regular course of practice.

In 1931 more than thirteen hundred Massachusetts physicians, joined by four hundred ministers and seven thousand laymen, petitioned the legislature to alter that state's Comstock Act and permit doctors to prescribe contraceptives. Among these physicians were such outstanding leaders of the profession as Drs. Shields Warren, Joe Vincent Meigs, Channing Frothingham, John Rock, Robert L. De Normandie, Howard B. Sprague, and George Gilbert Smith.

In 1937 the A.M.A.'s House of Delegates unanimously adopted a report of its Special Committee to Study Contraceptive Practices which recommended the promotion of instruction in medical schools on both contraception and infertility and urged the establishment of birth control clinics under medical supervision.

Through these and a long series of similar resolutions, petitions to legislatures, and court actions the medical profession established a proud record in defense of both its right and its duty to provide contraceptive information and to prescribe the means of contraception to all patients who wished to plan their families and space their pregnancies. By the early 1950s numerous court decisions had clearly established that right in almost every state. Even in Massachusetts and Connecticut, where the restrictive laws have not yet been repealed, no serious attempt was being made to enforce them.

Family planning, in fact, had ceased to be a taboo subject. It was discussed freely, not only in medical journals but in popular magazines, newspapers, and on television. It was endorsed by the leaders of every major religious grouping, though the Roman Catholic Church still opposes the use of "artificial" methods of family limitation and approves only the use of the rhythm method of limiting intercourse to the wife's infertile periods. So well had the medical profession done its educational job that numerous surveys showed that about eight out of every ten couples of childbearing age had adopted some method of spacing pregnancies and planning the size of their families.

This widespread adoption of contraception, however, had one unexpected, and regrettable, effect. Many of the conventional barrier-type contraceptives could be purchased without a physician's prescription. Others, such as diaphragms, required an initial visit to a physician for examination and fitting. But after that, many women failed to return for needed periodic re-examinations. Thus, all too often, couples denied themselves the benefits of their doctor's counsel on the choice of contraceptives and the methods of using them most effectively.

One of the major, though little noted, "side effects" of the development of the birth control pill was to reverse this unfortunate trend. Because oral contraceptives were 100 percent effective, millions of couples wanted to use them in preference to the less reliable and less esthetic older types of barrier contraceptives. But since the pills exerted their ovulation-inhibiting effect by physiological action, their use by some small classes of women was contra-indicated. In others, side effects had to be observed and controlled. Thus their utilization could be permitted only upon a doctor's prescription; a restriction which restored to both general practitioners and gynecologists their proper role as guardians of their patients' health and counselors on every aspect of family planning. Thousands of physicians, in fact, have found in the changed situation a new opportunity to practice effective preventive medicine.

In undertaking such positive, protective roles physicians are not arrogating to themselves a function unnatural to their profession. For the day has long passed—if indeed there ever was such a time—when medicine's sole function was to diagnose and treat already established diseases. To protect both their patients and their communities, doctors quite properly urge upon their patients an extremely wide range of preventive measures: vaccinations to protect against smallpox, polio, tetanus, diphtheria, measles, and other infections, X-rays to detect chest diseases in their earliest, most easily curable stages, premarital blood tests to prevent the transmission of venereal diseases, cytological "smear" tests to bring cancer to early treatment, diets to forestall the development of vascular diseases or to insure against nutritional deficiencies, and periodic physical checkups to reveal all sorts of deleterious conditions before they manifest themselves through the gross and painful symptoms of advanced and rampant disease. Thus, in not waiting passively until patients demand their advice on family planning, physicians are merely recognizing a new area in which their foresightedness can protect both their patients and society. In ever increasing numbers, doctors have accepted, as a professional responsibility, the duty of educating their patients about family planning and of prescribing the most effective means of contraception whenever sound medical, economic, eugenic, or social reasons make childbearing inadvisable.

Most married couples thus have been having no difficulty in obtaining from their own physicians both sound family-planning counsel and the means of applying it. But the situation has been a far different one for the poor who have no family doctors and must depend upon tax-supported hospitals, health departments, and welfare agencies for whatever medical services they receive. Until very recently, almost all of these public agencies have been either unwilling or unable to include family planning in their programs.

Yet it is precisely this segment of our population which most urgently needs family planning, both for its own welfare and for the health of our society as a whole. The birth rate among the rural and urban poor, who lack effective means of controlling their fecundity, has been as high as in the villages of India. For example, among recent impoverished migrants to Chicago, both Negroes and Southern whites, the birth rate has been more than thirty-seven per thousand people per year—nearly twice as high as that of their more fortunate fellow Chicagoans. As a result, a growing number of the poor—who might have been able to improve their situation by their own efforts if they had only two or three children—have been forced into permanent pauperism and dependency by their inability to support all the babies that have come to them. As their families increase, often at the full "natural" rate of a child a year, they become increasingly less able to give them the minimum of care essential to preserve health, provide adequate clothing and nutrition, and prevent the development of delinquency.

Even welfare programs—supplementing the parents' earnings with money from Federal, state, and local tax funds —fail of their purpose without birth control. In the last ten years the cost of maintaining the children of the poor, poorly, has soared to over $1.5 billion a year, because the number of children requiring aid has more than doubled.

Doctors, along with educators, social workers, and other thoughtful citizens, have long realized that if this vicious circle of self-perpetuating poverty is ever to be broken, the poor among us must be provided with the same opportunity to limit the size of their families which all the rest of us can obtain so easily through our family doctors. And, since the poverty-stricken often do not have family doctors and cannot afford to purchase contraceptive supplies, physicians and public health workers have long advocated the inclusion of family planning in the medical service programs of tax-supported health and welfare agencies.

For example, in 1959 the American Public Health Association—the national organization representing doctors, nurses, and social workers in public health agencies— adopted a policy statement which declared: "Serious public health problems are posed when family size impairs ability to sustain a healthful way of life, or when childbearing may adversely affect the health of the mother and her offspring. . . . Programs concerned with family size should be integral parts of health programs and should include medical advice and services which are acceptable to the individuals concerned. . . . Full freedom should be extended to all population groups for the selection and use of such methods for the regulation of family size as are consistent with the creed of the individuals concerned."

The American College of Obstetricians and Gynecologists—the national organization of physicians most intimately concerned with the health of mothers and their newborn—adopted a similarly strong resolution. The Chicago Gynecological Society voted that "Prescription of childspacing measures is an essential aspect of preventive medicine and should be available to all patients who desire it, whether they obtain their medical care through private physicians or through tax-supported health services."

The California Conference of Local Health Officers adopted a policy statement declaring, "Economic and educational circumstances should not deprive any family of equal access to family planning guidance and services. . . . Family planning is of public health concern if only because of the costly consequences to the rest of the community that arise from lack of such planning." The House of Delegates of the California Medical Association voiced the same position even more strongly in a resolution which stated: "The need for family planning exists in various socio-economic groups of the population. . . . Family planning services should properly be included in every medical care program."

The Academy of Medicine of Cleveland and the Cuyahoga County Medical Society jointly resolved that "Family planning advice is an integral part of good medical practice and should therefore be made available to all persons who desire it, through private physicians *and* tax- and community-supported health agencies."

In similar forthright phrasing, hundreds of other county and state medical organizations and specialists' societies have endorsed and urgently advocated the provision of contraceptive services by tax-supported hospitals and health departments. One of the firmest stands has been taken by the Trustees of the American Medical Association as the recognized spokesman for the entire medical profession. "There should be no restraint on the physician concerning the dissemination of birth control information," they declared. "As with other forms of quality medical care, such information should be equally available to both private and clinic patients."

Until just a few years ago, however, contraceptive information and supplies were available to the poor only through the privately financed clinics of the Planned Parenthood Federation and through some local health departments in seven Southern states. A 1958 attempt to win permission for physicians to prescribe contraceptives for the medically indigent patients of New York City's municipal hospitals aroused a storm of opposition from Catholic clergy and laymen, who feared that patients who were members of their faith would feel forced to accept contraceptive methods disapproved of by their creed. Only after many months of heated debate was a compromise reached in which it was agreed that all methods of family planning, including the rhythm method, would be offered so that the adherents of any faith would be able to choose a method in accord with their own conscience. It was also stipulated that no one— doctor, nurse, or patient—would ever be required to participate in a birth control program against his will.

214/

But in 1962 an attempt to make contraceptives available to the poor in Chicago—under restrictions similar to those already established in New York City—foundered under a storm of opposition. This time, in addition to religious objections, two other arguments were raised against the proposed program. The poor and poorly educated, it was asserted, would not be able to understand the proper use of contraceptives and would thus waste the supplies provided to them at public expense. Other opponents of the program insisted that its cost would unjustifiably raise the already high cost of welfare services and would thus impose an unfair extra burden upon the taxpayers.

Both of these arguments, however, were thoroughly deflated by a program started in 1960 in Mecklenburg County, North Carolina, by Welfare Director Wallace Kuralt and Assistant Public Health Director Dr. Elizabeth Corkey. Dr. Corkey previously had followed closely the reports of the clinical trials of Enovid in Puerto Rico, where many hundreds of poorly educated women had had no difficulty in mastering the pill-taking schedules. Thus, she and Mr. Kuralt decided to rely principally upon the pills when they announced that the Mecklenburg County Health Department clinics would provide contraceptive services to clients of the Welfare Department.

News of the new program spread like wildfire and the clinics were promptly besieged by hundreds of women anxious to limit the growth of their families. Ever since the first rush, additional women have voluntarily enrolled at an average rate of a dozen a week.

Dr. Corkey's program is thoroughgoing. When a woman first comes to the clinic she has a half-hour interview with a nurse. Then a doctor gives her a full physical examination, including a pelvic survey and a Papanicolaou smear test, to rule out any possibility that she has vaginal, cervical, or breast cancer. If the woman is healthy and elects to use the pills, the doctor prescribes them for her at county expense. Then a nurse describes to her how to mark a calendar so that she can maintain a regular pill-taking schedule.

Each of the nearly eight hundred women who enrolled in the program during its first four years had previously borne an average of more than five children; a few had had up to nineteen pregnancies. Yet, among all these women, not a single one became pregnant while using the pills.

As the program progressed its value in terms of family happiness and well-being became clearly apparent. With mothers freed to devote more time to the upbringing of their children, schools reported that the youngsters did better in class. The police noted a decline in new delinquency cases. The County Health Department found that these families were suffering fewer illnesses than before and requiring fewer medical services. Many families became entirely self-supporting and withdrew from the relief rolls.

In dollars-and-cents terms, the program has saved its cost to the County dozens of times over. The pills cost the Health Department less than $1 per patient per month. Individual examinations and periodic follow-ups approximately double this per-patient cost. But provision for the care of the nearly a thousand unwanted, dependent children who had not been born, would have cost the Welfare Department $30 per child per month, or approximately $360,000. "The health-and-welfare slice of the County budget has shrunk from 27 percent to barely 10 percent in the last four years," Mr. Kuralt reports. "For every dollar we have spent for the pills, we have effected demonstrated tax savings of $25 a year."

One of the most remarkable characteristics of the

Mecklenburg County program is the unanimous support it has gained from the community. "At no time has it interfered with the private practice of medicine," the Chairman of the County Medical Association states. "As doctors we know what women go through with multiple pregnancies, many of them unwanted; how they drag women down physically and emotionally. For this reason, we stand behind the clinics 100 percent."

Dr. Corkey and Mr. Kuralt, of course, were not the only public health workers who recognized that the development of oral contraceptives had opened up new opportunities to make family planning available to the poor. Almost as soon as the Food and Drug Administration authorized the use of Enovid as a contraceptive, in the spring of 1960, many other health department directors, public hospital administrators, and welfare officials began to plan the opening of contraceptive clinics.

The old barrier contraceptives, they knew, had frequently failed to prevent pregnancies even when used by the well-educated under medical guidance. For the poor, lacking adequate sanitary facilities and privacy, such devices as diaphragms promised an equal or even higher failure rate. But the Puerto Rican experience had proved that the pills were acceptable to most women irrespective of social status and that they could be used effectively even by people living in poor and crowded circumstances.

Moreover, the once hush-hush subject of family planning had been brought out into the open; and extensive discussion of the new pills, by every medium of mass communication, was rapidly bringing about great changes in public thinking. The public and the press could be expected to consider bold new programs objectively and rationally.

In a few places, most notably in Chicago, attempts to extend family planning services to the poor ran into stormy Roman Catholic opposition and suffered temporary setbacks. But the attitudes of both Catholic clergy and laymen were themselves undergoing profound changes. Without approving the use of "artificial" contraceptives by their own communicants, Catholic communities had begun to take an increasingly broad view of the need for family planning. As the Rev. John A. O'Brien, S.J., Research Professor of Theology at Notre Dame University, declared, "Citizens of all faiths must unite to remove this nettlesome issue from the political and social life of our nation. Catholics, Protestants, and Jews are in agreement over the objectives of family planning. It would be well to settle the policy of public hospitals and health agencies with respect for the rights of conscience of all concerned."

Thus, as the problem of making family planning equally available to all economic groups has become increasingly separated from social and political controversy, the number of tax-supported hospitals, health departments, and welfare agencies providing birth control services has doubled and redoubled. In New York City, fourteen municipal general hospitals and seven health department clinics now offer family planning guidance and supplies. Baltimore, Detroit, Philadelphia, Augusta (Georgia), Portland (Oregon), Corpus Christi, Dallas, Milwaukee, and the District of Columbia have similar programs in operation and are rapidly expanding them. As this is written, more than four hundred cities and counties in twenty-seven states have made contraceptive pills available to their poor.

Wherever these programs have been instituted their results have duplicated, almost in exact detail, the Mecklenburg County experience. The overwhelming majority of poor women have eagerly welcomed the new services and quickly demonstrated their ability to use the pills effectively. Gains in family welfare and stability have been manifest. And the programs everywhere have saved their own cost many times over, by reducing expenditures for the support of dependent children.

Despite this obvious progress, however, the sad fact remains that so far barely 10 percent of all our poor have been brought into the community of Americans to whom contraceptive knowledge and supplies are freely available. A Federal Advisory Council, for example, has recently criticized the "skittishness" of the Department of Health, Education and Welfare and urged upon it a rapid expansion of Federal support for state and local family planning programs.

The logic of this position can hardly be disputed in a country that is embarking upon a multi-billion-dollar War on Poverty. For, amidst all the expenditures which this "war" will require—for better housing, new schools, retraining for the unskilled, etc., etc., etc.—no program will require so little money nor produce such substantial and rapid progress toward the elimination of poverty as will the extension of contraceptive knowledge and supplies to all who need and want them.

14

•

PILLS, POLITICS, AND THE POPULATION EXPLOSION

•

In 1798 a solemn young British curate named Thomas Malthus got into a heated argument with his father and with the political philosopher William Godwin. These older men saw—in the American and French revolutions and in the Industrial Revolution already gathering steam in England— the beginnings of an era of increasing progress and prosper-

220/ THE HORMONE QUEST

ity for mankind. But to young Malthus these hopes seemed utterly unfounded. He insisted that the progress Godwin and other optimists were anticipating would be halted by an inexorable law of nature. And he felt so strongly about it that he sat down and expounded his theory in a pamphlet entitled "An Essay on the Principle of Population As It Affects the Future Improvement of Society."

Malthus' line of reasoning was simple. He argued that food supplies (or as he called it, subsistence) increased only in an arithmetic ratio—1, 2, 3, 4, etc.—while population tended to multiply in a geometric ratio—1, 2, 4, 8, 16, etc. Thus, he declared, population would always tend to increase far faster than the means of subsistence until halted by the inevitable checks of war, pestilence, or famine. Any improvements in mankind's productive capacity—such as the already invented steam engine and cotton spinning and weaving machines—would, this grim prophet insisted, merely increase the sum total of human misery by permitting a larger population to exist in the same state of impoverishment as before the change was introduced.

Malthus' "Essay" touched off more than thirty years of vehement controversy. Some used it to argue against all attempts to ameliorate the social evils that accompanied the early phases of the Industrial Revolution. To end child labor, shorten the fourteen-hour workday, raise wages, or even to lighten the miseries of the poor through doles or charity, would, they insisted, only encourage the impoverished to breed faster and thus create a surplus of laborers doomed to unemployment and starvation. But many others, from the poet Shelley to such reformers as Francis Place, denounced Malthus' dismal theory as cruel and unscientific nonsense, serving only to excuse a complete and callous disregard for the woes of the poor.

By the mid-nineteenth century, however, emigration was draining millions of Europe's poor to America. Increasing industrialization was producing a notable rise in the general standard of living. European birth rates began to fall instead of rising as Malthus had predicted. As the wheat of the United States and Canada, the beef of the Argentine, and the mutton of Australia flowed into Europe, history itself seemed to be disproving Malthus' argument that population would always outrun subsistence. Eventually both Malthus and his theory were relegated to mere footnotes in economic histories or ignored entirely.

Shortly after World War II demographers and other social scientists began to note a new phenomenon. In the more highly developed countries, as a result of a host of improvements in medicine and in sanitation, the death rate had been declining for more than a century. But during the war and immediately afterward, new drugs, such as penicillin, and new insecticides, such as DDT, had brought about a precipitate drop in the death rate, not only in the advanced countries but even more notably in the less industrialized areas of Asia, Africa, and South America.

In Ceylon, for example, the death rate had been twenty-two per thousand in 1945. Then, by the use of widespread airplane spraying of DDT, malaria was all but completely wiped out. By 1950 the death rate had fallen to eleven per thousand, a reduction of 50 percent in just five years.

In Japan our occupation forces and the local authorities had immunized nine million against typhus, thirty-four million against cholera, sixty million against typhoid, and had inoculated eighteen million children against diphtheria. Within only five years these public health measures had cut the death rate to less than half its prewar level.

In British Guiana the infant death rate in the slum-festered capitol Georgetown stood at over 140 per 1,000 in 1945, primarily because of insect-borne diseases. Then, for three years, public health officers dusted a ten-mile circle about the town with DDT. By 1948 infant mortality had fallen by more than half.

In India the postwar death rate fell one third below its prewar level; in Venezuela it was cut in half; in Puerto Rico it was reduced by over 60 percent. Even in the advanced countries of Europe and in the United States, already low death rates declined by between 10 and 40 percent between 1945 and 1950.

But while death rates were declining at an unprecedented pace, birth rates failed to follow this trend. In the economically advanced countries they soared; in the underdeveloped countries, where they had previously decreased little if at all, they remained at their old peak levels or rose still higher.

By 1950 the results of this rapidly widening gap between death and birth rates were clearly apparent to demographers: what could only be termed a population explosion was occurring at a tremendous and rapidly accelerating pace. Where the world's population had been growing by about ten million a year before World War II, it was now increasing at an annual rate of twenty-five million or more. And unless something effective was done to bring birth rates down, the very kind of disaster that gloomy Malthus had envisioned would sooner or later take place.

In this country and elsewhere a number of social scientists tried to alert the public and its leaders to this looming threat. In 1948 Fairfield Osborn, president of the New York Zoö-logical Society, published *Our Plundered Planet;* the ecol-

ogist William Vogt, national director of the Planned
Parenthood Federation, wrote his *Road to Survival;* in 1951
Robert C. Cook's *Human Fertility: The Modern Dilemma*
became a best-seller for a time.

Because these books did point out that population growth
was indeed outracing the food supply, numerous critics
labeled their authors "Neo-Malthusians" and charged them
with attempting to scare the world by reviving an old and
long-disproved doctrine of doom. In doing so, however,
they ignored one vital difference between Malthus' theory
and the views of men like Osborn, Vogt, and Cook. Malthus
had maintained that any substantial population expansion
would inevitably be checked by war, famine, or pestilence.
But Osborn, Vogt, Cook, and their colleagues were pro-
posing that mankind not wait for these disasters to occur.
Instead they urged that the population explosion be arrested
by deliberately limiting human fertility. To counterbalance
the effects of "death control" they urged the world-wide
adoption of birth control.

At first, these proposals won only limited support. But
during the 1950s, as the world's population continued to
grow at an ever increasing rate, many who once had scoffed
at the very idea of a population crisis changed their views.
Typical was the case of one of our most distinguished
scientists, Dr. Vannevar Bush. In 1950 he had dismissed the
problem as something chemists and technologists would
take care of by opening tropical areas to cultivation. But
only four years later his outlook had undergone a profound
change: "Man is headed for catastrophe," he declared. "The
world's population is increasing at a rate which renders
distress, famine, and disintegration inevitable unless we learn

to hold our numbers within reason. New methods of extending the food supply, powerful though they may be, can only postpone the crisis."

All over the world thousands of other scientists, social scientists, public health workers, and physicians also began to press for action. Yet with only a few exceptions politicians and statesmen—who alone could initiate any effective population control measures—continued skittishly to avoid the problem, largely because they feared offending the sensibilities of those who opposed some methods of family limitation on religious grounds. Thus, throughout the 1950s, while the world's population grew by nearly half a billion and the increment of new mouths to feed rose from twenty-five million to over fifty million a year, so-called "demographic conferences" and "population studies" served as sorry substitutes for the birth control information and supplies needed everywhere.

Then, in 1959, a distinguished commission headed by General William H. Draper was appointed to review the U.S. foreign aid program under which we had been spending up to $5,000,000,000 annually to help underdeveloped nations improve their economies and raise the standard of living of their people. In country after country these investigators found that all the value of our financial assistance was being wiped out by enormous rises in population. Instead of increasing, per capita incomes were standing at their old low levels and, in some countries, were actually falling.

But this commission was not content merely to assemble a set of statistics to be quietly filed and forgotten. In its report to President Eisenhower it grasped the nettle others had repeatedly avoided and boldly recommended that the United States help countries that requested our aid "in the formulation of their plans designed to deal with the problem of rapid population growth."

In Congress, in the press, and over radio and TV, the Draper Report evoked wide discussions of both population problems and birth control. Thousands who had never spoken out before voiced their strongest support for the committee's recommendations. But the Catholic bishops of the United States announced that they would oppose any public program to promote birth control at home or abroad. Thus, when President Eisenhower was queried about the Draper Report at a press conference, he closed the door to any action by declaring: "I cannot imagine anything more emphatically a subject that is not a proper political or governmental activity or function or responsibility. . . . This government has not, and will not, as long as I am here, have a program that has to do with birth control. That's not our business."

During his first years in office President Kennedy made no public departure from the position taken by his predecessor. In launching his Alliance for Progress program, for instance, he set as a goal the lifting of per capita income in Latin America by not less than 2.5 percent a year. But in country after country, the program fell far short of this target because our administrators were forbidden to use any part of our hundreds of millions of dollars of aid funds for birth control projects.

In the six nations of Central America, for example, population grew in both 1961 and 1962 by more than 4 percent a year. As a result per-capita incomes in Costa Rica, El Salvador, Honduras, and Nicaragua actually fell despite the influx of American funds. Even in Guatemala and Panama, where national incomes rose slightly, the standard of living of the poor with growing families underwent a marked decline. In Venezuela, where the population grew by 4.4 percent a year, the annual income of the average citizen in 1962 was $25 less than it had been five years earlier. In Argentina the runaway growth of population resulted in a drop in per capita income of more than 7 percent in a single year.

The tragic meaning of these statistics can be appreciated only when they are translated into human terms. In the capital of Honduras women too poor to purchase a blanket have had to leave the maternity hospital with their babies wrapped in old newspapers. Because of malnutrition of mothers and their babies the infant mortality rate in Guatemala was the highest in the world. Nicaragua was unable to provide even elementary schooling for nearly two thirds of its child population. Thus, despite all our economic aid, the price of uncontrolled fertility in most of Latin America proved to be continuing and increasing poverty, illiteracy, hunger, and disease.

But while our national government was thus pouring billions so ineffectually into foreign aid programs, a new factor began drastically to change public attitudes both here and abroad. In the Puerto Rican and Haitian field trials oral contraceptives had proved their acceptability and their effectiveness under the most adverse of conditions. And when, in May, 1960, the Food and Drug Administration approved the marketing of the pill for contraceptive use, more than a hundred thousand American women immediately besieged their doctors to obtain prescriptions. Thus the pill was put to a new and crucial test, not just by a few thousand women under carefully controlled experimental circumstances, but by vast numbers, most of whom had adopted it in preference to the contraceptives they had previously used. If it significantly reduced the birth rate among these women—white and Negro, rich and poor, college graduates and semi-literates—there would be no remaining doubt that the world at last had a method of contraception capable of halting the population explosion.

Public Health Service statisticians have several methods of measuring the fecundity of a population. The most commonly cited is the birth rate, which reflects the number of births occurring annually per thousand members of the entire population, male and female and of all ages. A much more sensitive index is the fertility rate: the number of babies born for each thousand women of childbearing age, fifteen through forty-four years. Such fertility rate figures are compiled monthly by the National Center for Health Statistics of the U. S. Public Health Service. By the end of 1961 the first slight signs of the pill's mass effectiveness began to appear as the fertility rate fell by eight tenths of a point, from 118.0 to 117.2.

Every month since then—as the number of users of oral contraceptives has swelled to more than five million—the fertility rate among American women has dropped below the figure for the same month of the preceding year. The annual fertility rate for 1962 was 112.1, more than five points lower than in 1961. In 1963 the fertility rate fell to 108.4. In 1964 the decline in births carried the fertility rate down to 105.8. In January of 1965 (the last month for which figures are available as this is written) the fertility rate stood at only 95.7: a decline of nearly 20 percent in barely four years.

So great, in fact, has been this fall in the fertility rate since the introduction of oral contraceptives, that it has more than counterbalanced the growth of the number of women of childbearing age and produced a sharp decline in the total number of births. In 1961, when there were approximately 36,800,000 women between 15 and 44, 4,268,-000 births were recorded. In 1964, when the number of potential childbearers had risen to 39,500,000, only 4,045,-000 babies were born, the smallest number for any year since 1953.

As millions of American women and tens of thousands of their physicians were thus demonstrating the ability of oral contraceptives to effect a drastic reduction in population growth, the traditional taboos against government action in this area began to crumble. At first these changes were purely local, as city and county welfare and health commissions began to provide oral contraceptives to the medically indigent. But in December of 1962 President Kennedy signaled the beginning of a change at the Federal level when he authorized our United Nations delegation to support a proposal to permit the UN to provide birth control assistance to countries requesting it.

A year later former President Eisenhower dramatically reversed his previous stand. "When I was President," he wrote in *The Saturday Evening Post*, "I opposed the use of federal funds to provide birth control information to countries we were aiding because I felt this would violate the deepest religious convictions of large groups of taxpayers. As I now look back, it may be that I was carrying that conviction too far. . . . The time has come when we must take into account the effect of the population explosion on our mutual-assistance program. A large proportion of this increase is occurring in countries which are having difficulty in feeding and clothing their present populations and desperately need a little elbow room while they improve their resources. . . . There is no real progress or security to a nation which, with outside help, raises its productive capacity by two percent a year while the population rises by three percent. . . . I want to stress the responsibility we have for finding some realistic means of containing this human explosion."

Still another small step toward a change in our national policy was taken in 1963, when Congress passed and President Kennedy signed the first foreign aid bill to authorize the use of funds for population studies. Then, in 1964 and early 1965, the dams against effective Federal action to halt the population explosion broke on both the domestic and foreign aid fronts. As President Johnson asked Congress to pass his war against poverty program, Sargent Shriver told Congressional committees that communities would be free to use Federal funds supplied through the Office of Economic Opportunity to provide local birth control services. And in his January, 1965, State of the Union message President Johnson placed his stamp of approval on a final and definitive change of policy with an unmistakably explicit one-sentence declaration: "I will seek new ways to use our knowledge to help deal with the explosion in world population and the growing scarcity in world resources."

Only one day later the implementation of that promise began, as the Office of Economic Opportunity issued its first approval of a birth control facility under the antipoverty program: a grant to help establish part-time contraceptive clinics in eight impoverished neighborhoods of Corpus Christi, Texas. Two days after the President's message the U. S. Children's Bureau allotted $1,500,000 to help New York City finance nine maternal health clinics providing a complete range of family planning services. Numerous additional allocations have since been made to set up

230/   THE HORMONE QUEST

or expand similar projects, providing both contraceptive instruction and supplies, in many cities and rural areas.

Abroad, as in this country, the advent of the pill has stimulated broad and far-reaching actions designed to slow down the growth of populations and permit the achievement of a rising standard of living. In Egypt, for example, President Nasser long opposed birth control, hoping instead to accommodate his country's growing millions on the two million acres of land to be made fertile by the waters impounded by the Aswan High Dam. But in 1962 he realized that before the new dam could be completed, Egypt's annual 3-percent population increase would crowd every new acre as densely as the rest of the Nile Valley. "We have added 800,000 persons to our number this year," he declared. "We cannot go on at this rate. It has become the duty of the state to advise the people on methods of birth control." Ever since then the Egyptian Ministry of Public Health has been purchasing oral contraceptives in bulk and redistributing them, at low cost or free, through a growing chain of clinics manned by physicians and social workers.

Japan, which halved its birth rate during the 1950s by means of legalized abortions, has now changed its policy and has established more than eight hundred "eugenic protection consultation offices" to popularize adequate methods of contraception. Oral contraceptives are thus coming into ever wider use.

In Chile, in 1961, a committee of leading epidemiologists estimated that between 125,000 and 150,000 illegal abortions were being performed annually. In that year fifty-four thousand women had to be admitted to hospitals for treatment of the massive hemorrhages, infections, or internal injuries brought on by such abortions. So alarming were these figures that, in 1962, as oral contraceptives became available, the country's Public Health Service appointed a National Committee for the Protection of the Family, which has since opened contraceptive clinics in six Santiago hospitals and others in Concepción, Antofogasta, Temuco, and other regional centers.

Attempts by the Swedish Ceylon Family Planning Project to introduce the use of rubber or chemical barrier contraceptives among the poorly educated laborers in Ceylonese tea plantations failed. But since 1961, under the direction of Dr. Siva Chinnatamby, a large-scale oral contraceptive project among illiterate Tamil tea pickers has produced a decline of over 50 percent in the birth rate.

In Thailand, Korea, and Pakistan substantial new government-sponsored contraceptive programs have been put into effect since 1962. In Hong Kong, Taiwan, Ceylon, and several Latin American countries, similar projects have been initiated by voluntary agencies with government support. As this is written Tunisia's Health Ministry has announced the establishment of twelve contraceptive and family planning clinics, the first units of a chain intended, eventually, to reach every area in the country.

While one after another of these projects has greatly reduced birth rates among participating women, none of the underdeveloped countries as yet has managed to launch a program large enough to cut down substantially its overall rate of population increase. The world's population, which passed the three billion mark in 1962, is thus currently growing by more than sixty million every year.

Yet this situation, which seemed so hopeless only a few years ago, no longer need be regarded as one that defies solution. For the advent of the pill has not only given mankind a new weapon with which to control its destiny. It has also effected a revolutionary change in the thinking and the actions of political, social, and religious leaders all over the world. For this country, which has seen the benefits of nearly $70,000,000,000 of foreign-aid funds largely nullified by the population explosion, science has provided a new opportunity to help end forever the burdens imposed by uncontrolled human fertility.

15

•

THE UNFINISHED
BUSINESS OF HORMONE
RESEARCH

•

When Professor George Redmayne Murray first demonstrated, seventy-four years ago, that an extract of the thyroid of a sheep could prolong the life of a women suffering from thyroid deficiency disease, he inspired a few dozen physicians and physiologists to envision the possibility of relieving other diseases by what we now call replacement therapy.

When, barely sixty years ago, Drs. William Starling and Ernest Bayliss coined the word hormone to help clarify their concept of a whole system of glandular secretions that regulated bodily functions, they stimulated first hundreds and, ultimately, many thousands of physicians, biologists, and chemists into a search for these powerful substances and for ways of using them effectively to relieve human ills.

Since then no branch of medicine and its related sciences has expanded more rapidly nor produced more profound effects upon the health and well-being of mankind; effects which, as we have seen, extend today far beyond the control of disease and are deeply influencing social and economic developments.

It would not be unreasonable, therefore, to wonder whether the hormone quest has not already passed its peak of productivity; whether most of the major discoveries in this field have not already been achieved, leaving only minor improvements in the techniques of hormone synthesis and endocrine therapy yet to be accomplished.

Fortunately, such is far from the case. Instead, every advance in our knowledge about hormones has had the "side effect" of revealing to scientists and clinicians vast new areas inviting exploration. As Dr. Gregory Pincus has described the situation, "The progress of hormone research has made it ever more apparent that there is no stage in human development, from conception to senility, which is exempt from hormonal influence. Thus, for a long, long time to come, hormones will continue to be inciters of scientific curiosity and stimulants to investigation. To judge from the scientific rewards that have already been reaped, there are far greater rewards to come."

To hasten the realization of these potentialities, such organizations as the American Cancer Society, the American Heart Association, and the National Foundation, and such governmental agencies as the National Institutes of Health have been devoting ever increasing millions to the support of hormone research. And virtually every major pharmaceutical house here and abroad has been expending more time, money, and man power on laboratory and clinical hormone studies than on any other class of drugs.

Let us examine, therefore, where the cutting edge of endocrine research stands today and what sober, conservative, and cautious scientists and clinicians are striving to achieve, not in some distant future, but, hopefully yet realistically, within the next two decades or even sooner.

During the first weeks after conception the human embryo is entirely dependent for its hormones on transfers from its mother's blood stream to its own via the placenta. Any imbalance in the mother's endocrine system thus may adversely affect the development of the fetus. Birth defects in babies born to diabetic mothers, for example, are about ten times more frequent than in the infants born to non-diabetics.

Until fairly recently physicians could do little to prevent these disasters. Today, however, a number of measures are being used increasingly widely and successfully. With frequently repeated tests physicians are able to adjust dosages of insulin or of the newer oral anti-diabetic drugs, so as to compensate for the changing needs of both mother and fetus. During early pregnancy they may increase the amount of insulin the mother receives. But once the infant's islets of Langerhans develop and begin to secrete insulin— usually during the fourth or fifth month of gestation—the amount of insulin given the mother may have to be reduced.

In many seemingly normal women the stresses of pregnancy may suddenly trigger off a latent diabetic state, thus endangering the health or even the life of the mother, the fetus, or both. Routine urine tests often in the past have failed to reveal such sub-clinical or "pre-diabetic" conditions at early prenatal examinations. But much more sensitive tests—of blood rather than urine—are now being widely used. At the Prenatal Clinics of New York's Mt. Sinai Hospital, for example, the number of such pre-diabetic patients identified early in pregnancy by blood tests now represents more than half the Clinics' total case load.

Even more recently clinical researchers have found that disturbances of the secretions of other hormones often occur in diabetic women during pregnancy. For example, investigators have reported a marked decrease in estrogen output in many pregnant diabetics and some have claimed a significant decline in fetal defects as a result of administering large doses of estrogen to diabetic women throughout pregnancy. Other workers have reported unusually low progesterone-excretion levels among diabetic mothers-to-be and therefore have suggested the administration of both progestins and estrogens as a protective measure for mother and fetus. Neither of these hypotheses is yet regarded as fully proven. But, both are being carefully explored at a number of research centers and hospitals.

The study of the fetal development of all the endocrine glands, in fact, has become a rapidly developing sub-specialty of gynecologic endocrinology. Abnormalities in the maturation of the fetal pituitary, for example, have been found to have marked effects on the growth of the embryo's thyroid, adrenals, and gonads. These deficiencies or delays of glandular development in turn affect other phases of prenatal growth and thus often result in the birth of babies with pronounced mental or physical defects.

Today, doctors are able to ameliorate some of these defects by prompt postnatal therapy. The administration of thyroid hormones to a hypothyroid newborn infant, for example, can prevent it from developing into a cretin. But an increasing number of clinical researchers are seeking new ways of detecting disturbances of an embryo's gland function at an early stage in its development. If they can do so, it may become possible to forestall failures of glandular development by hormone therapy while the fetus is still in the womb.

Meanwhile, other investigators have been finding that some causes of severe illness or death among the newborn are, as had not previously been known, caused or aggravated by prenatal hormonal deficiencies. For example, hyaline membrane disease—the pulmonary condition that caused the death of the late President Kennedy's infant son —afflicts some forty thousand American infants annually. It manifests itself as a gathering of thick mucus upon the walls of the tiny air ducts of the infant's lungs until—often within twenty-four hours after delivery—the baby suffocates.

This deadly disease was believed, until recently, to result from the accidental inhalation during delivery of amniotic fluid from the fetal bag of waters. But noting that hyaline membrane disease is particularly common among premature babies and those delivered by Caesarian section, Drs. Douglas Shanklin of the University of Florida and Sorrell L. Wolfson of Tampa General Hospital developed the hypothesis that the condition might actually be caused by the estrogen deprivation such babies undergo in the womb; a deprivation which in turn causes a weakening of capillary blood vessels in the lungs with a resultant flow of fluid that gradually blocks the smaller air passages. Supporting this hypothesis was the fact that male infants, who normally have lower estrogen levels, develop the hyaline disease twice as frequently as do females.

To test their hypothesis Drs. Shanklin and Wolfson tried estrogen injections in "last resort" attempts to save a number of babies facing imminent death from suffocation. In seven out of nine such cases, they reported, the infants pulled through; a far higher survival rate than has been achieved under previous methods of treatment with oxygen administered under pressure. If further studies confirm and extend these first extremely favorable results, several new avenues of therapy may be developed. For newborn infants, doctors may administer estrogen injections at the first signs of pulmonary difficulty. Or, as a preventive measure, obstetricians might find it desirable to build up estrogen levels in women with a history of premature delivery or when pelvic measurements indicate the necessity for terminating pregnancy by Caesarian operation.

Extreme instances of abnormal growth patterns—dwarfism or gigantism—are fortunately rare. But many millions of us are handicapped throughout life by lesser deviations from the norm. The boy who fails to grow beyond the height of five feet, for example, is inevitably barred from numerous occupations and thus faces a lifetime of limited economic opportunities. The girl who is nearly six feet tall faces not only difficulties in obtaining suitable clothes and shoes, but also markedly diminished chances of marriage. The extremely thin and the excessively obese of both sexes not merely suffer social handicaps, but are also far more susceptible to numerous forms of disease. Thus it has long been a goal of medical research to develop some means of controlling and correcting abnormal patterns of growth.

More than forty years ago hopes were raised high by an experiment conducted by Dr. Herbert M. Evans at the University of California at Berkeley. He removed the pituitary glands of two young dachshunds. In one, to whom nothing else was done, growth came to a halt. But Dr. Evans injected into the other dog a crude extract he had prepared from canine pituitary glands. Under its influence this second dog's bones, muscles, and fatty tissues continued to grow as if he had never been operated upon. At maturity he was twice the size of his unfortunate litter mate. Thus Dr. Evans demonstrated definitively what others had only previously suspected, that the pituitary secreted a growth-stimulating hormone.

For a short time it seemed that Dr. Evans' discovery had indeed opened up the long-sought possibility of increasing human stature. But when extracts of dog, sheep, or hog pituitaries were tried on dwarfed humans, they proved fruitless. Later research disclosed that the growth hormones of these animals differed so greatly from human growth hormone as to make them utterly ineffective. Then, in 1956, hopes were raised once again when Dr. Choh Hao Li, Dr. Evans' protégé and successor at the University of California Hormone Research Laboratory, succeeded in isolating highly purified growth hormones from the pituitary glands of monkeys and of humans. These substances proved effective in stimulating the growth of people suffering from pituitary failures. But since it required more than a hundred pituitary glands to provide enough hormone to maintain a single patient under treatment, the application of this fantastically rare and expensive substance was necessarily restricted to experimental use upon the most extreme cases of dwarfism.

One hope of at least partially overcoming this difficulty
has stemmed from a plan now being worked out, in both
the United States and Canada, to facilitate the collection of
human pituitaries from autopsies. The possibility of synthesizing the pituitary growth hormone has long seemed a
dim one because the substance is an extremely complex
protein. In recent years, however, Dr. Li and his co-workers
have succeeded in discovering the precise sequence of amino
acids which make up the chain-like structure of the growth
hormone. Intensive efforts are currently under way to re-
create this structure in the laboratory. If and when these
efforts succeed, they will provide physicians with an extremely powerful and effective tool that may help hundreds
of thousands of growth-retarded youngsters to achieve a
normal or near normal stature.

Since the time of Dr. Evans' classic dachshund experiment, endocrine researchers have discovered that the pituitary growth hormone is only one of a number of hormones
capable of affecting growth processes. While the pituitary
alone seems to play the major role in stimulating growth
from birth to the age of about twelve, a second spurt of
growth normally follows the coming into activity of the
sex glands at puberty. In young girls, for example, ovarian
estrogens not only stimulate breast and genital development,
they also cause the bones to grow in length for a period of
from three to four years. By the end of this time, the
estrogens have closed off the growing ends of the bones—
the epiphyses. Thus, in a perfect instance of nature's econ-
omy, the same hormone that causes girls to grow so fast
during puberty also brings height increases to a halt when
puberty ends.

A number of endocrinologists have found in this phenomenon an opportunity to prevent the development of

excessive tallness in girls with an unusually fast rate of growth, by using large doses of estrogen to bring about early epiphyseal closure. One of the pioneers in this work was Dr. Max A. Goldzieher. In eleven of fourteen patients, he was able to hold further growth down to an average of one inch by the use of estrogen therapy. Dr. Robert B. Greenblatt, of the Medical College of Georgia, and a number of other endocrinologists have confirmed and extended Dr. Goldzieher's work.

When estrogens alone are used for this purpose, however, excessive menstrual bleeding often occurs. To avoid this complication, a number of experimenters have also used progestins toward the end of the menstrual cycle. Periodic X-rays are made to note the progress of bone-end closure. From nine months to one year of treatment is sufficient, in most cases, to halt further growth.

Under the control of skilled endocrinologists, this form of therapy has seemed thus far to produce no major ill effects. However, until a sufficient number of experimentally treated girls have been observed over a period of years and found to have suffered no loss of fertility or other long-term ill effects, most physicians wisely discourage the general adoption of such growth-halting treatment.

Ideally, the perfect substance to halt excessive growth would be a synthetic steroid which would retain estrogen's bone-end-closing potentiality but lack other estrogenic qualities. The hope that such a steroid may yet be synthesized has been greatly increased since the development of the anabolic compounds in which testosterone's tissue-building properties have been retained and enhanced while its androgenic activities have been virtually eliminated.

These synthetic anabolic agents have also opened up prospects for the development of another form of growth control. While they have already come into wide use to stimulate protein metabolism and the redevelopment of wasted muscles, they have also been observed to have some effect upon fat metabolism. Thus, at a number of research laboratories, chemists and biologists are synthesizing and testing similar compounds in the search for one that will, as it were, "discourage" the deposition of excessive fat without causing undesirable side effects.

While endocrinologists have scored many successes in relieving infertility, one recent development has served to emphasize the prospect of achieving far greater advances within the next few years. It has long been known that ovulation is under the control of a follicle-stimulating hormone secreted by the pituitary gland. In a fairly substantial number of women infertility results from their pituitaries' failure to produce or release an adequate supply of this hormone.

In 1957 Dr. Carl Gemzell of the Medical School of the University of Uppsala in Sweden developed a method of extracting the follicle-stimulating hormone from human pituitaries obtained at autopsy. Injecting this into some fifty non-ovulating patients, he was able to cause ovulation in more than half of these women, most of whom became pregnant after from one to six courses of treatment. About 1960, in Rome, Dr. Pietro Donini discovered a way of extracting and purifying the same hormone from the urine of post-menopausal women. In this country the Cutter Laboratories of Berkeley, California, have been providing Dr. Donini's extract—called Pergonal—for experimental use at a number of hospital-affiliated fertility clinics.

At the Columbia-Presbyterian Medical Center in New York, for example, fifteen of twenty-one women treated with the extract have become pregnant. Similar results have been achieved by Dr. Janet McArthur at the Massachusetts General Hospital in Boston, by Dr. Eugenia Rosemberg of the Worcester City Hospital Research Laboratories, and at the Tyler Fertility Clinic in Los Angeles. In some patients, however, the new extract has evoked a number of undesirable side effects. Some women have experienced allergic reactions. In others, experimenters have felt that it promoted the development of ovarian cysts.

Perhaps its strangest effect is its tendency to cause the simultaneous release of more than one ovum. In every experimental group of patients treated to date, the proportion of multiple births has been far greater than among normally ovulating women in the general population. In the Swedish series reported by Dr. Gemzell, nearly half of the women who became pregnant delivered twins and two conceived quadruplets. Of the first seven pregnancies completed by women treated with the extract at the Columbia-Presbyterian Hospital, three produced twins and another gave birth to quadruplets.

By no means do all women regard this pronounced tendency to cause multiple births as undesirable. After six to eight years of fruitless striving for motherhood, many welcome the prospect of "catching up" by having two or more babies at once. Some gynecologists, however, point out that such multiple pregnancies heighten the risks of miscarriage and of complications in labor. Enthusiasts for the new preparation, on the other hand, feel that instances of "super ovulation" are the result of overdose and that as more is learned about how and when to administer the drug, the incidence of multiple births may be reduced to no more than that which occurs under natural conditions. Meanwhile, Pergonal has not yet—as this is written—been approved by the Food and Drug Administration and thus can only be used by approved clinical investigators.

The development of the new extract has, however, had another effect: it has encouraged greatly intensified efforts to develop synthetic compounds capable of inducing ovulation, either by direct stimulation of the ovaries or by restoring the pituitary's normal output of its natural follicle-stimulating hormone. In fact, one such drug, a steroid derivative, is already undergoing experimental clinical tests, and a number of others are in various stages of development. The hope is that such synthetic hormones will be able to cause single-ovum ovulation and be free of allergic and other side effects.

Arteriosclerosis, or hardening of the arteries, is the greatest single cause of disability and death. In atherosclerosis, its most common form, fatty substances—and particularly cholesterol—accumulate upon the inner surfaces of arteries, reducing their blood-carrying capacity and hardening the artery walls so that they lose their normal elasticity. In the arteries feeding the heart, such restriction of blood flow often manifests itself in the excruciatingly painful paroxysms of angina pectoris. When blood blockage becomes severe enough, the victim often suffers a myocardial infarction, or heart attack, which, if it does not cause immediate death, may destroy areas of heart muscle and thus invite later, deadly attacks.

In the brain, the reduction of the blood supply often brings about an increasing impairment of mental functions. And when fragments of atherosclerotic tissue break off from the arterial lining, these emboli may completely block a vital blood vessel in the brain and cripple or kill their victim by a stroke.

Cholesterol itself is essential to many metabolic processes. But because it plays so large a role in the development of atherosclerosis, fighters against this disease long concentrated their efforts upon attempts to lower cholesterol levels in the blood in the hope of preventing its accumulation upon arterial walls or even of reversing the degenerative process and bringing about a reduction of the already accumulated artery lining deposits. Diets relatively free from saturated fats, for example, have been widely used to reduce the blood's cholesterol content. These efforts, however, have often fallen far short of attaining their desired effect because the body itself converts other substances into cholesterol. Thus, more recently, the attention of many investigators has shifted toward efforts to restore to the body its normal ability to maintain a proper balance of the blood's content of cholesterol and other fats or lipids.

Very strong evidence exists that the mechanism by which cholesterol is held in proper balance is largely under the control of the female sex hormones. The death rate from atherosclerosis among men, for example, rises rapidly from the age of thirty-five onward. In women, on the other hand, atherosclerosis is an extremely rare phenomenon until the menopause reduces their output of estrogens. Postmenopausal women develop atherosclerosis with increasing frequency and their death rate from this disease rises with their age until ultimately it closely approaches that of males.

Further confirmation of the importance of estrogens in preventing the development of atherosclerosis has come from studies of women who have undergone operations for the removal of their ovaries. Deprived of ovarian estrogens, these women develop abnormally high blood cholesterol levels and experience the end results of atherosclerosis—

angina pectoris, heart attacks, strokes—with almost the same rate of incidence as men of similar age.

To ward off or halt or slow down the development of atherosclerosis in women who have undergone ovariectomies and in post-menopausal women, clinicians have naturally turned to the administration of estrogens to replace the natural hormone they no longer produce. A number of studies have found such replacement therapy to be effective.

With equal logic, attempts have been made to use estrogens in the treatment of male victims of atherosclerosis. Almost all such efforts, however, have been frustrated because long-term estrogen therapy exerts numerous feminizing influences upon men. Their breasts develop. Their beards grow thin. Some become sexually impotent. Thus, even men who have already suffered one or more heart attacks often prefer to run the risk of a fatal attack rather than accept the feminizing side effects of the estrogens which might extend their lives.

To circumvent this therapeutic quandary, steroid chemists have been trying for a number of years to synthesize modified estrogens—compounds capable of exerting the cholesterol-controlling effects of these hormones but free from the estrogens' feminizing side effects. A large number of compounds have displayed this desired separation of properties in experiments on animals; a few have exhibited the same effects in clinical trials on humans. But their administration has, unfortunately, been accompanied by other side effects—on the liver, for example—which have interdicted their widespread use.

Yet these apparent failures have clearly demonstrated the possibility of the creation of a truly useful anti-atherosclerosis steroid. Thus the search has not only continued, it has been expanded. At the National Institutes of Health, at the Worcester Foundation for Experimental Biology, and in the research laboratories of most major pharmaceutical houses large numbers of chemists and biologists are devoting their efforts to the synthesis and testing of an ever broadening range of non-feminizing, lipid-shifting steroids.

As far back as 1940 Dr. Charles Huggins, Chief of the Department of Urology of the University of Chicago Hospitals, gave synthetic estrogen pills to a man suffering from advanced prostate cancer. Within a few days, the patient was able to get out of bed. After further doses, he left the hospital and went back to work. Dr. Huggins and his associates had demonstrated, for the first time in a human being, the ability of a hormone to bring about a remission of cancer.

Not long after this pioneer experiment, testosterone was found capable of bringing about remissions in a substantial proportion of cases of inoperable breast cancer, causing tumors to decrease in size, lessening pain, and giving patients a feeling of vigorous well-being. Still later it was discovered that estrogenic hormones could induce breast cancer remissions in post-menopausal patients.

Since then more than fifty synthetic steroids have been found useful in the treatment of these most common types of cancer. Like other chemotherapeutic agents, they do not cure the disease. But in thousands of cases, they have substantially extended useful lives and freed patients from intractable pain.

Today the search for even more effective hormones for the treatment of cancer is co-ordinated by the Cancer Chemotherapy National Service Center, a division of the

National Institutes of Health. The laboratories of such pharmaceutical houses as G. D. Searle & Co. submit all newly synthesized compounds, after preliminary biological screening, to the Endocrine Evaluation Branch of the Cancer Chemotherapy Center for more definitive tests against tumors in mice.

Many of these compounds, of course, fail to display sufficient anti-tumor activity to make them preferable for use over already known steroids. But every year a few demonstrate high potencies and are prepared in kilogram quantities for clinical testing upon cancer patients. This gradual increase in both the number and the effectiveness of anti-cancer steroids, though unspectacular, is of much greater importance than one would at first suppose. For physicians have discovered that tumors that grow refractory to one steroid may undergo a new remission when treatment by another steroid of quite similar structure is prescribed.

The broader hope, obviously, is that some as yet undiscovered steroids or other synthetic hormones may prove capable of producing much longer or even permanent remissions, not only of breast and prostate cancers but of other forms of cancer as well.

Late in the fifth decade of every human life the activity of the endocrine glands—and particularly of the gonads —begins to diminish. In men the output of testosterone may decline very gradually, sometimes over several decades. In women this climacteric change often takes place within a year or two, as some still to be understood biological clock ends ovulation, permits the ovaries to shrink, and ultimately manifests itself in a whole series of adverse physical and emotional changes generally lumped under the name of the menopause.

With advancing age both sexes become more like each other. As Dr. William H. Masters, of the Washington University School of Medicine, describes it: "A third sex exists and is rapidly multiplying in our society. This so-called 'neutral gender' is made up of previous members of both the male and female sexes who have reached an approximate age of sixty years."

Until about a generation ago almost all physicians looked upon these changes of the menopause and the male climacteric as normal, if regrettable, processes—the beginning of the degenerations of old age against which no active therapy could hope to prevail. But one early and ardent dissenter from this view was the late Dr. Fuller Albright of the Harvard Medical School. Nearly a quarter of a century ago he urged the active use of hormonal therapy to prevent such post-menopausal disorders as osteoporosis. But, a prophet before his time, Dr. Albright found little acceptance for his ideas in the 1930s.

Today, however, a growing school of physicians have come to regard both the male climacteric and the menopause as diseases than can and should be relieved by sex-steroid therapy. Dr. Allan Barnes, Professor and Chairman of the Department of Obstetrics and Gynecology of The Johns Hopkins School of Medicine, for example, has declared: "In my practice the menopause is a disease process requiring active intervention." And Dr. Robert A. Wilson, Consulting Obstetrician and Gynecologist of the Methodist Hospital of Brooklyn, writes, "In the past, so-called mental 'adjustment' to the 'change of life' was necessary. There was no choice. Without such adjustments, the ensuing years were hardly endurable. . . . But, today, we know that menopausal women are not normal; they suffer from a deficiency disease with serious sequelae and need treatment."

Such views, which many other physicians are rapidly adopting, have been justified by the development of a series of new and successful therapeutic applications of the adrenal and gonadal steroid hormones. Thus, today, a number of endocrinologists prescribe testosterone or its synthetic analogs for many of their male patients who have passed their middle fifties, to forestall mild depressions, inability to concentrate upon their work, and other emotional or physical manifestations of diminished sex hormone secretion. Dr. Robert Greenblatt, for example, has closely observed a number of such patients over a period of years. As long as he has supplied them with testosterone, most have reported a return of vigor and vitality; they are convinced that they feel better, work more effectively, and get more enjoyment out of life.

But, with true scientific skepticism, Dr. Greenblatt has not been content to accept these patients' reports at face value. Periodically he has given a number of these men placebos instead of the hormones they had previously been receiving, and in instance after instance they have returned to him—often within a few days—to say, "Something is wrong, doctor. The drug is no longer working." Thus their reports of well-being cannot be written off as merely the psychological response to pill-taking. Their bodies force them to distinguish between the active hormone and a placebo.

"Mind you," warns Dr. Greenblatt, "I'm not suggesting that these androgens are achieving rejuvenation. We're not getting any Brown-Séquard effect. What is much more likely is that the anabolic tissue-building action of these agents is keeping these men in a better state of health and thus enabling them to function better and feel better."

Such generalized replacement therapy, however, is by no

means the only new recourse to which physicians can turn to aid their older male patients. A number of the common disabling conditions that frequently accompany the male climacteric have become directly susceptible to steroid treatment. After the age of fifty, for example, approximately one man in three suffers from hypertrophy, or enlargement, of the ring-like prostate gland which surrounds the neck of the bladder. This non-malignant overgrowth usually causes painful difficulty in urination, and in severe cases may actually prevent normal emptying of the bladder. Because of such obstruction, and the infections that often accompany it, many patients experience kidney damage and some develop arterial hypertension.

Until recently doctors had only two choices to offer victims of prostate hypertrophy. As long as the condition was bearable, they could choose to live with it. When it became insufferable, surgical removal of the prostate was prescribed. Today doctors are being armed with a far better alternative in the form of newly developed steroids capable of inhibiting prostate enlargement.

For menopausal and post-menopausal women, men like Dr. Wilson and Dr. John L. Bakke, Associate Professor of Medicine at the University of Washington School of Medicine in Seattle, advocate active therapeutic intervention through the cyclic use of progestin-estrogen combinations. Their goal, of course, is not to inhibit ovulation, since it would not occur in any event among women in this age group. Instead they seek, by hormone-replacement therapy, to protect these women from the metabolic changes that otherwise accompany ovarian atrophy.

Such changes include a loss of calcium and protein in the bones which may result in osteoporosis; a shrinking in height; the development of so-called dowager's hump; a loss of the normal female protection against atherosclerosis; a tendency to gain weight and to develop diabetes in those who have the inherited trait; a withdrawal of protein from the skin, thinning it and causing the fine wrinkles usually blamed on aging; a vasomotor instability evidenced in hot flushes; and, in many women, a persistent, severe, and recurring itching.

"These are not the changes of aging," Dr. Bakke states. "They are the metabolic changes of ovarian failure or castration. Just as we can correct the metabolic defects in thyroid failure by using thyroid hormones, so we should correct ovarian failure with ovarian hormones and thus prevent or retard the metabolic changes listed above."

Thus hormone researchers, from chemists to clinicians, are busier today than ever before. They are driven not only by personal or professional ambition but by a vision of imminent possibilities of benefiting humanity in innumerable ways. Undoubtedly, the fulfillment of some of their hopes may be delayed. Some may even fail of fulfillment. But if history provides any guide to the future, the hormone quest of the next decade will make all its past discoveries pale by comparison.

INDEX

Barbasco, 54–5, 56
Barnes, Allan, 249
Bayliss, William Maddock, 18–20, 21, 45, 234
Baylor University School of Medicine, 145
Beatty Institute, Chester, 41
Bernard, Claude, 10–13, 16, 20
Berthold, Arnold Adolph, 3–5, 7–8, 15, 28
Best, Charles A., 25–27
Biedl, Artur, 8
Biosynthesis, 75
Birth control, xiii, 111–13, 204, 207, 211; anti-, 203–4; development of compounds, x; politicians and, 224–6, 228–30, 232; population explosion and, 223–232; in Ceylon, 231; in Japan, 230; in Korea, 231; in Pakistan, 231; in reverse, 148–66; in Thailand, 231; in Tunisia, 231 see also Family planning
Birth defects, 235
Birth rate, 220–21, 222, 227, 230–232
Blackwood, W. R. D., 205
Bordeu, Théophile, 7
Borno, Raymond, 134
Boston University School of Medicine, 107
Bouin, Paul, 34
Breslau, University of, 34
Bright, Richard, 23
British Medical Journal, 142
Bronchial asthma, 18, 80
Brown, Edward A., 104
Brown, Samuel S., 88
Brown-Séquard, Charles Édouard, 13–16, 20, 21
Browne, John Symonds, 173, 174
Brownell, Katherine, 60
Bryan, John B., 106
Budapest, University of, 176
Burket, Robert, 144
Burns, severe, 80, 93
Burtner, Robert R., xiv, 104
Bush, Ian, xiv, 96
Bush, Vannevar, 223–4
Butenandt, Adolf, 32, 35, 36, 44

Calciuria, 88
California Conference of Local Health Officers, 212; —Medical Association, 212; —, University of (Berkeley), 37, 239; —, University of, School of Medicine 135
Cancer, xii, xiii, 139–41, 146, 247–248
Cancer Chemotherapy National Service Center, 247
Capon-comb test, 22, 35, 36
Carnegie Institute, 176
Cartland, George F., 62
Cary William H., 204
Castration, effects of, 4–5
Cella, John A., 103, 104
Chang, Min-Chueh, xi–xii, 115, 116, 122
Chicago Gynecological Society, 212; —, University of, 35, 71, 83, 168; —University Hospitals, 247
Childlessness, involuntary, 149
Chile, birth rate in, 230–31
Chinnatamby, Siva, 231
Chobanian, Aram V., 107
Cholesterol, 30, 31, 32, 37, 44, 244, 245
Ciba, xii
Cincinnati General Hospital, 144
Cirrhosis, hepatic, 108
Clark University, xi
Cleveland Academy of Medicine, 212; —Clinic Hospital, 107
Clowdus, Bernard F., 107
Collip, James B., 40
Colton, Frank B., xiv, 85, 90, 91, 121, 122, 196–7, 198
Columbia-Presbyterian Medical Center, New York, 242, 243
Columbia University, 61, 63; —College of Physicians and Surgeons, 186
Competitive inhibitors, 101–2
Compound A, Kendall's, 63–4
Compound E, Kendall's, 64, 65–66
Compound F, 64
Comstock, Anthony, 202–4
Comstock Act and laws, 203–8

 **ABOUT THE AUTHOR**

ALBERT Q. MAISEL has been principally interested, as a writer, in medicine and public health, especially their social aspects. Over the years his articles on these subjects have appeared in *Reader's Digest, Life, Look, McCall's, Ladies' Home Journal,* and other magazines. His experience during World War II as a correspondent specializing in medical activities resulted in three books: *Miracles of Military Medicine, Africa,* and *The Wounded Get Back.* Mr. Maisel's articles exposing conditions in Veterans' Hospitals were responsible for a Congressional investigation and eventual reform. His exposure of conditions in state mental hospitals (in *Life* and *Reader's Digest*) brought about similar reforms in many states and won him the 1951 Lasker Medical Journalism Award. His most recent book, *They All Chose America* (1957), was based on an expanded series of *Reader's Digest* articles concerning the influence of various ethnic groups in the development of America's culture and history. Mr. Maisel, the father of two grown children, lives with his wife in Ridgefield, Connecticut.